22nd Chinese National Conference on Computational Linguistic (CCL 2023)

Tutorial Abstracts

Harbin, China
3 - 5 August 2023

ISBN: 978-1-7138-8991-5

Printed from e-media with permission by:

Curran Associates, Inc.
57 Morehouse Lane
Red Hook, NY 12571

Some format issues inherent in the e-media version may also appear in this print version.

Printed with permission by Curran Associates, Inc. (2024)

For permission requests, please contact the Association for Computational Linguistics at the address below.

Association for Computational Linguistics
209 N. Eighth Street
Stroudsburg, Pennsylvania 18360

Phone: 1-570-476-8006
Fax: 1-570-476-0860

acl@aclweb.org

Additional copies of this publication are available from:

Curran Associates, Inc.
57 Morehouse Lane
Red Hook, NY 12571 USA
Phone: 845-758-0400
Fax: 845-758-2633
Email: curran@proceedings.com
Web: www.proceedings.com

The 22nd Chinese National Conference on Computational Linguistics: Tutorial Abstracts

Tutorial Abstracts

August 3 - August 5, 2023

Harbin, China

Order copies of this and other CCL proceedings from:

Chinese National Conference on Computational Linguistics (CCL)

Courtyard 4, South Fourth Street, Zhongguancun , Haidian District, Beijing

100190, China

Tel: + 010-62562916

Fax: + 010-62661046

cips@iscas.ac.cn

Introduction

Welcome to the tutorial session of CCL 2023.

The tutorial session is a pivotal part of our conference, curated to equip our attendees with a holistic understanding of pertinent topics within our dynamic and ever-evolving research landscape. This is achieved by leaning on the expertise of accomplished researchers in the field who painstakingly share insights drawn from their valuable experiences.

Large Language Models (LLMs) such as ChatGPT have significantly influenced the trajectory of NLP research. Acknowledging this profound impact, this year we have centered our tutorial session around the pivotal theme of LLMs. We are delighted to have four insightful tutorials on the agenda. Two of these focus on the knowledge analysis, extraction and enhancement, ethical considerations, and safety concerns associated with LLMs. The remaining two take an interdisciplinary approach, delving into the study oflanguage processing in the human brain with speech and language models, and the innovative application of LLMs in the realm of robotics.

We express our deepest gratitude to the authors of these tutorials for their dedication and hard work. Their efforts are fundamental to the success of this session. Our appreciation also extends to the conference organizers for their immense support and their essential role in coordinating this event.

It is our sincere hope that these tutorials will prove both enlightening and enjoyable, providing the knowledge and inspiration to fuel further innovative endeavors in the field.

July 2023

Yang Feng, Peng Li

Organizers

Tutorial Chairs

Yang Feng	Institute of Computing Technology, Chinese Academy of Sciences, China
Peng Li	Tsinghua University, China

Table of Content

预训练语言模型中的知识分析、萃取与增强

陈玉博，曹鹏飞，王晨皓，李嘉淳，刘康，赵军 ······ 1

Safety and Ethical Concerns of Large Language Models

Zhiheng Xi, Rui Zheng, and Tao Gui ······ 9

Studying Language Processing in the Human Brain with Speech and Language Models

Chao Zhang, Andrew Thwaites, Cai Wingfield ······ 17

Foundation Models for Robotics: Best Known Practices

Shaocong Xu, Hao Zhao ······ 24

预训练语言模型中的知识分析、萃取与增强

陈玉博[1,2], 曹鹏飞[1,2], 王晨皓[1,2], 李嘉淳[1,2], 刘康[1,2,3], 赵军[1,2]
[1]中国科学院自动化研究所复杂系统认知与决策实验室
[2]中国科学院大学人工智能学院
[3]北京智源人工智能研究院
{yubo.chen, pengfei.cao, chenhao.wang, kliu, jzhao}@nlpr.ia.ac.cn

摘要

近年来，大规模预训练语言模型在知识密集型的自然语言处理任务上取得了令人瞩目的进步。这似乎表明，预训练语言模型能够自发地从语料中学习大量知识，并隐式地保存在参数之中。然而，这一现象的背后机理仍然萦绕着许多谜团，语言模型究竟掌握了哪些知识，如何提取和利用这些知识，如何用外部知识弥补模型不足，这些问题都亟待进一步探索。在本次讲习班中，我们将重点介绍在预训练语言模型知识分析、知识萃取、知识增强等领域的近期研究进展。

关键词： 预训练语言模型 ； 知识分析 ； 知识萃取 ； 知识增强

时长： 90分钟

目标听众： 目标听众主要为自然语言处理领域和知识图谱领域的研究人员和工程人员，听众将在本次讲习班中了解预训练语言模型相关的知识分析、知识萃取、知识增强等领域的最新研究进展。

内容大纲：

- 预训练语言模型简介（5分钟）
- 预训练语言模型的知识分析（包括知识的探测、定位和编辑）（40分钟）
- 预训练语言模型的知识萃取（从预训练语言模型提取符号知识）（15分钟）
- 预训练语言模型的知识增强（用外部知识辅助预训练语言模型）（30分钟）

Knowledge Analysis, Extraction and Enhancement in Pre-trained Language Models

Yubo Chen[1,2], Pengfei Cao[1,2], Chenhao Wang[1,2], Jiachun Li[1,2], Kang Liu[1,2,3], Jun Zhao[1,2]
[1]The Laboratory of Cognition and Decision Intelligence for Complex Systems
[2]School of Artificial Intelligence, University of Chinese Academy of Sciences
[3]Beijing Academy of Artificial Intelligence
{yubo.chen, pengfei.cao, chenhao.wang, kliu, jzhao}@nlpr.ia.ac.cn

Abstract

Recently, large-scale pre-trained language models have made remarkable progress in knowledge-intensive natural language processing tasks. It seems to indicate that pre-trained language models can naturally learn extensive knowledge from the corpus and implicitly encode it in the parameters. However, the underlying mechanisms behind the phenomenon remain largely unknown. Questions such as what knowledge has been acquired by language models, how to extract and utilize the knowledge, and how external knowledge can be incorporated to address the limitations of models, are

第二十二届中国计算语言学大会论文集，第1页-第8页，哈尔滨，中国，2023年8月3日至5日。

all awaiting further exploration. In this tutorial, we will focus on introducing recent research advancements in the knowledge analysis, knowledge extraction, and knowledge enhancement of pre-trained language models.

Keywords: Pre-trained Language Models , Knowledge Analysis , Knowledge Extraction , Knowledge Enhancement

Duration: 90 minutes

Targeted Audience: The target audiences are researchers and engineers in the field of natural language processing and knowledge graph. In this tutorial, the audiences will learn about the latest research progress in knowledge analysis, knowledge extraction, and knowledge enhancement related to pre-trained language models.

Outline:

- Introduction of Pre-trained Language Models (5 minutes)
- Knowledge Analysis in PLMs (Knowledge Probing, Locating and Editing) (40 minutes)
- Knowledge Extraction in PLMs (Extracting Symbolic Knowledge from PLMs) (15 minutes)
- Knowledge Enhancement in PLMs (Assisting PLMs with External Knowledge) (30 minutes)

1 内容介绍

近年来，预训练语言模型已逐渐成为自然语言处理领域的基座模型。相关实验现象表明，预训练语言模型能够自发地从预训练语料中学到一定的语言学知识、世界知识和常识知识，从而在知识密集型任务上获得出色的表现(AlKhamissi et al., 2022; Safavi and Koutra, 2021; Petroni et al., 2019)。然而，预训练语言模型中的知识隐式地存储在参数之中，难以显式地对预训练语言模型中的知识进行分析和利用。同时，预训练语言模型在知识和推理上的表现并不可靠，常常会出现"幻觉"现象(Ji et al., 2022)，给出与知识冲突的预测结果。这些因素阻碍了预训练语言模型提供可靠的知识服务。因此，探究模型掌握知识的机理、研究如何提取和补充语言模型中的知识成为近期的研究热点。

本次讲习班主要内容包括预训练语言模型中的知识分析、预训练语言模型的知识萃取、知识增强的预训练语言模型三个部分，听众将在本次讲习班中了解到近期研究中对预训练语言模型掌握知识情况的认识、从预训练语言模型中提取符号知识的实现方案、利用外部知识增强模型弥补缺陷的各类方法。

1.1 知识分析

预训练语言模型在预训练阶段学习了大量语料，并隐式地从中获取了多种类型的知识。然而，这些知识的存在状态对人类来说是不透明的。我们很难直接确定预训练语言模型掌握了哪些知识，也并不清楚确定这些知识所在的位置和访存机制。因此，想要更好地研究预训练语言模型中的知识，势必要对语言模型进行深入的知识分析。

首先，为了确定预训练语言模型中存在哪些知识，需要进行最基本的知识探测工作。知识探测的基本思想是用已经整理好的人类知识，检验模型掌握的程度。目前，互联网上公开可用的知识资源可以大致分为语言学知识、世界知识、常识知识三类(Wang et al., 2021a)。对于这三类知识，现在已经有一些在预训练语言模型之上的探测分析工作，可以大体分为有训练方法和无训练方法。语言学知识方面，相关工作主要使用语言模型的隐层表示进行语言结构预测，检查对语言结构知识的掌握程度(Liu et al., 2019)；或直接通过提示模型进行生成，探测模型是否掌握词汇关系知识(Jain and Anke, 2022)。世界知识方面，相关工作主要依托现有三元组形式的知识库构造知识补全任务，并通过特定提示词引导模型预测，探测语言模型正确预测结果的能力(Petroni et al., 2019; Jiang et al., 2020; Shin et al., 2020; Liu et al., 2021a)。常识知识方

第二十二届中国计算语言学大会论文集，第1页-第8页，哈尔滨，中国，2023年8月3日至5日。

面，相关工作主要依靠打分对比判断的形式，分析模型能否正确区分句子是否符合常识(Zhou et al., 2020; Li et al., 2022)。这些研究工作表明，语言模型一定程度上拥有不同种类的知识。但是，由于语言模型知识探测结果可能受到多种因素干扰，目前的研究尚不足以可靠地确定语言模型拥有知识的范围，仍然需要更有效的实验设计(Cao et al., 2021a)。

除了从整体上探测语言模型掌握知识的能力表现。另一类语言分析研究试图从语言模型结构中定位出与特定类型知识相关的部分，从而更深入地理解语言模型访存知识的机制。目前在这方面最主要的假设是语言模型各层的前馈网络模块起到了类似键值存储的作用(Geva et al., 2021)。有关研究证明了不同层的前馈网络模块能识别不同程度的语义信息，并且前馈网络的隐层表示、变换矩阵参数与世界知识能否正确补全有较强的因果联系(Dai et al., 2022; Meng et al., 2022a)。这些研究初步实现了对部分知识的存储位置定位，从整体角度说明了在语言模型中，特定类型的知识可能存储于局部参数之中，调整这些参数能对语言模型的知识表现产生影响。

此外，预训练语言模型的知识来自于训练语料，并固化在模型参数之中。尽管模型可以通过训练获取新的知识，但这一过程往往会引入对旧知识的灾难性遗忘，难以控制。因此，在分析预训练语言模型的知识范围、存储位置基础上，另一类最新研究正在探索定向编辑语言模型中的知识。这些工作旨在有效编辑目标知识的同时，尽量保持无关知识不受到影响，大体上可以分为超网络方法和定向知识编辑方法。前者主要依靠数据驱动方法和元学习思想，训练一个根据知识编辑内容产生模型更新参数的超网络，从而满足知识编辑的优化目标(Cao et al., 2021b; Mitchell et al., 2022)。后者主要在知识定位分析的基础上，确定知识存储形式和预期更新结果，然后通过局部更新的方法实现知识的有效编辑(Dai et al., 2022; Meng et al., 2022a)。目前，知识编辑的研究正在逐渐扩大规模(Meng et al., 2022b)，但是仍然存在知识类型有限、难以连续更新等问题。

1.2 知识萃取

预训练语言模型中蕴含着大量知识，但这些知识隐式地存储在模型参数之中，难以直接访问和量化分析。此外，目前构造结构化知识库是一项耗时耗力的任务，语料中蕴含的许多知识可能至今尚未得到结构化组织。因此，随着预训练语言模型的知识能力不断进步，越来越多的研究工作试图将语言模型中的隐式知识萃取出来，得到符号化显式表达的知识，用于进一步分析和应用。

由于常识知识收集难度高，且现有知识资源严重不足，因此当下的知识萃取工作更多在常识知识上开展。这些方法主要将知识萃取过程分解成多个子任务，每个子任务依靠提示引导预训练语言模型进行生成或判别，从而获取大量结构化知识候选。这些结构化知识候选再通过进一步的过滤得到高质量的知识集合。在模型基础能力强，萃取流程设计合理的情况下，预训练语言模型能够用于产生质量与人类相当的常识知识(West et al., 2022)。最新的知识萃取方法正在逐渐放宽对预训练语言模型要求的条件(Wang et al., 2022; Bhagavatula et al., 2022)，并且将萃取实践扩展到世界知识在内的更多知识类型上(Cohen et al., 2023)。

1.3 知识增强

近些年来，预训练语言模型暴露出来的推理能力不足、产生幻觉等现象愈发受到人们重视(Ji et al., 2022)。知识增强作为缓解这些问题的重要方法，在近年来有一系列深入研究。

第一类知识增强方法主要从预训练目标任务设计的角度考虑问题。由于早期预训练语言模型大多基于掩码重建任务进行预训练，所以采用知识引导的掩码策略来引入知识成为一种较为直接的知识增强方式。例如，百度ERNIE(Sun et al., 2019)引入了短语级和实体级的掩码粒度，将额外的知识融入到掩码语言模型任务学习中。Graph-Guided MLM(Shen et al., 2020)采用了一种知识图谱引导的掩码策略，筛选出信息量更高的实体以高效地学习KG中的结构化知识。除此之外，一些工作还提出了更多样化的预训练任务，如KALM工作中的Knowledge-Aware任务(Rosset et al., 2020)、KEPLER中的知识表示损失(Wang et al., 2021c)、百度ERNIE 3.0工作中的多层次知识相关任务等(Sun et al., 2021)。

第二类知识增强方法主要从模型结构设计的角度考虑问题。在现有基础模型之上增加知识注入的相关模块，以显式的方式将知识融合入模型中。例如通过修改模型输入端设计，增加新的Knowledge Embedding层，在输入端将知识结构表示与原有的文本信息结合编码，典型工作包括K-BERT(Liu et al., 2020)、CoLAKE(Sun et al., 2020)等。另一些工作则是引入额外

第二十二届中国计算语言学大会论文集，第1页-第8页，哈尔滨，中国，2023年8月3日至5日。

的模块编码知识信息，并通过信息交互融合模块在深层将文本和知识信息融合，典型工作包括清华ERNIE(Zhang et al., 2019)，KG-BART(Liu et al., 2021b)，KnowBERT(Peters et al., 2019)等。

第三类知识增强方法主要从外部模块交互的角度考虑问题。上述两类方法都改变了预训练语言模型原有的任务或结构，需要针对性的训练，从而将外部知识注入到模型之中。随着模型的复杂化和参数量的增加，其灵活性欠缺和训练成本偏高的缺点也逐渐被放大，这催生了基于外部模块交互的知识增强方法。此类方法在尽量不修改基础模型的前提下，开发与基础模型解耦的知识增强模块，通过优化该模块实现知识增强，具有成本低、可扩展等特点。例如，K-ADAPTER(Wang et al., 2021b)将小型的知识模型以插件的形式连接到语言模型上，通过小模型的学习向其中注入特定知识。KGLM(IV et al., 2019)借助动态的本地小型知识图谱，在生成阶段不断补充相关知识。此外，最新研究也逐渐扩展到GPT-3、ChatGPT这类千亿参数的超大规模语言模型上，通过微调或提示设计等方式，让语言模型学会生成操作指令，与搜索引擎、数据库等外部知识工具交互，从中得到与输入文本相关的知识，作为模型的补充输入解决知识相关的任务(Nakano et al., 2021; Peng et al., 2023)。

2 推荐阅读列表

本次讲习班主要涉及预训练语言模型背景下的知识工程研究，在相关领域有一些优秀的综述性文章。

1. 预训练语言模型用于知识密集型自然与语言处理任务(Yin et al., 2022)
2. 预训练语言模型的工作机理、知识分析(Rogers et al., 2020; AlKhamissi et al., 2022)
3. 预训练语言模型中的知识探测、增强方法(Safavi and Koutra, 2021)
4. 融合外部知识资源的技术综述(Wang et al., 2023)

3 讲者介绍

陈玉博，中国科学院自动化研究所副研究员，研究方向为自然语言处理和知识图谱，在ACL、EMNLP、AAAI 等国际重要会议和期刊发表学术论文40 余篇，其中多篇论文入选Paper Digest最具影响力论文，曾获多次最佳论文奖（NLP-NABD 2016、CCKS 2017、CCL 2020、CCKS 2020），Google Scholar引用量4100余次。出版学术专著两部《知识图谱》、《知识图谱：算法与实践》，由人工智能学会推荐入选十三五国家重点图书出版规划教材，连续多年在中国科学院大学主讲《知识图谱》课程，2021 年获得中国科学院大学优秀课程。主持国家自然科学基金面上项目、青年基金项目，参与国家自然科学基金重点项目、2030新一代人工智能重大项目、重点研发计划课题。主持研发的信息抽取和知识图谱构建系统多次获得国际/国内学术评测冠亚军。入选2020 年第五届中国科协青年人才托举工程、2022 年全球华人AI 青年学者、2022 年中国科学院青年创新促进会会员、2022北京智源人工智能青年科学家俱乐部，担任中国中文信息学会青年工作委员会秘书长、COLING 2022领域主席、Data Intelligence编委等。获2018 年中国中文信息学会"钱伟长中文信息处理科学技术奖"一等奖（个人排名第四），2019 年度北京市科学技术进步奖一等奖（个人排名第五）。

4 其他贡献者介绍

本讲习班的其它贡献者有：

赵军，中国科学院自动化研究所研究员，博士生导师；中国科学院大学人工智能学院岗位教授。研究领域为自然语言处理、知识图谱、信息抽取、问答系统、大模型等。作为项目负责人承担国家自然科学基金重点项目、科技创新2030-新一代人工智能重大项目等多项国家级重要科研项目以及企业应用项目。在ACL、IJCAI、SIGIR、AAAI、COLING、EMNLP、TKDE等顶级国际会议和重要学术期刊上发表论文100余篇，曾获第25届国际计算语言学大会COLING 2014最佳论文奖，Google Scholar引用量19000余次。出版学术专著两部《知识图谱》、《知识图谱：算法与实践》，由人工智能学会推荐入选十三五国家重点图书出版规划教材，连续多年在中国科学院大学主讲

第二十二届中国计算语言学大会论文集，第1页-第8页，哈尔滨，中国，2023年8月3日至5日。

《知识图谱》课程，2021 年获得中国科学院大学优秀课程，获朱李月华优秀教师奖。主持研发的“大规模开放域文本知识获取与应用平台”获得2018年中国中文信息学会“钱伟长中文信息处理科学技术奖”一等奖，主持完成的“大规模知识图谱构建关键技术与应用”项目获得2019年度北京市科学技术进步奖一等奖。兼任中国中文信息学会常务理事，语言与知识计算专委会副主任，《中文信息学报》编委，Machine Intelligence Research （MIR）编委等学术职务。

刘康，中国科学院自动化研究所研究员、博士生导师，中国科学院大学岗位教授，北京智源人工智能研究院青年科学家。研究领域包括自然语言处理、文本信息抽取、知识图谱、问答系统等。在自然语言处理、知识工程等领域国际重要会议和期刊发表多篇学术论文，Google Scholar引用16000余次，单篇引用数达到2700余次，H-Index为50。2020-2023连续入选Aminer ”AI 2000人工智能全球最具影响力提名学者。曾获COLING 2014最佳论文奖、Google Focused Research Award（2015、2016）、中国中文信息学会“汉王青年创新一等奖”、中国中文信息学会“钱伟长中文信息处理科学技术奖”一等奖、北京市科学技术进步一等奖等多项学术奖励。2019年获得国家自然科学基金委优秀青年基金支持，2020年入选中国科学院青年创新促进会优秀会员。目前兼任中国中文信息学会理事、中国中文信息学会计算语言学专委会、中国中文信息学会语言与知识计算专委会秘书长等学术职务。目前担任Pattern Recognition、TACL等学术期刊编委，也曾任ACL、AAAI、EMNLP、CIKM、ISWC、EACL等国际高水平学术会议（Senior）Area Chair/Senior PC member。

曹鹏飞，中国科学院自动化研究所助理研究员。主要研究方向为自然语言处理、知识图谱、信息抽取。以一作身份在AAAI、ACL、EMNLP等人工智能领域国际顶级学术会议上发表多篇论文。曾任中国中文信息学会青年工作委员会学生执委会的执行委员，中国自然语言处理学生研讨会的博士生论坛主席，并担任TKDE、ACL、EMNLP、AAAI等著名国际期刊和学术会议的审稿人。

王晨皓，中国科学院自动化研究所2019级硕博生。主要研究方向为知识图谱、常识知识获取与知识探测、常识推理。并在AAAI、EMNLP、CCKS等人工智能领域学术会议发表多篇论文。

李嘉淳，中国科学院自动化研究所2022级直博生。主要研究方向为常识知识获取与知识探测。

参考文献

Badr AlKhamissi, Millicent Li, Asli Celikyilmaz, Mona T. Diab, and Marjan Ghazvininejad. 2022. A review on language models as knowledge bases. *CoRR*, abs/2204.06031.

Chandra Bhagavatula, Jena D. Hwang, Doug Downey, Ronan Le Bras, Ximing Lu, Keisuke Sakaguchi, Swabha Swayamdipta, Peter West, and Yejin Choi. 2022. I2D2: inductive knowledge distillation with neurologic and self-imitation. *CoRR*, abs/2212.09246.

Boxi Cao, Hongyu Lin, Xianpei Han, Le Sun, Lingyong Yan, Meng Liao, Tong Xue, and Jin Xu. 2021a. Knowledgeable or educated guess? revisiting language models as knowledge bases. In Chengqing Zong, Fei Xia, Wenjie Li, and Roberto Navigli, editors, *Proceedings of the 59th Annual Meeting of the Association for Computational Linguistics and the 11th International Joint Conference on Natural Language Processing, ACL/IJCNLP 2021, (Volume 1: Long Papers), Virtual Event, August 1-6, 2021*, pages 1860–1874. Association for Computational Linguistics.

Nicola De Cao, Wilker Aziz, and Ivan Titov. 2021b. Editing factual knowledge in language models. In Marie-Francine Moens, Xuanjing Huang, Lucia Specia, and Scott Wen-tau Yih, editors, *Proceedings of the 2021 Conference on Empirical Methods in Natural Language Processing, EMNLP 2021, Virtual Event / Punta Cana, Dominican Republic, 7-11 November, 2021*, pages 6491–6506. Association for Computational Linguistics.

Roi Cohen, Mor Geva, Jonathan Berant, and Amir Globerson. 2023. Crawling the internal knowledge-base of language models. *CoRR*, abs/2301.12810.

Damai Dai, Li Dong, Yaru Hao, Zhifang Sui, Baobao Chang, and Furu Wei. 2022. Knowledge neurons in pretrained transformers. In Smaranda Muresan, Preslav Nakov, and Aline Villavicencio, editors, *Proceedings of the 60th Annual Meeting of the Association for Computational Linguistics (Volume 1: Long Papers), ACL 2022, Dublin, Ireland, May 22-27, 2022*, pages 8493–8502. Association for Computational Linguistics.

第二十二届中国计算语言学大会论文集，第1页-第8页，哈尔滨，中国，2023年8月3日至5日。

Mor Geva, Roei Schuster, Jonathan Berant, and Omer Levy. 2021. Transformer feed-forward layers are key-value memories. In Marie-Francine Moens, Xuanjing Huang, Lucia Specia, and Scott Wen-tau Yih, editors, *Proceedings of the 2021 Conference on Empirical Methods in Natural Language Processing, EMNLP 2021, Virtual Event / Punta Cana, Dominican Republic, 7-11 November, 2021*, pages 5484–5495. Association for Computational Linguistics.

Robert L. Logan IV, Nelson F. Liu, Matthew E. Peters, Matt Gardner, and Sameer Singh. 2019. Barack's wife hillary: Using knowledge graphs for fact-aware language modeling. In Anna Korhonen, David R. Traum, and Lluís Màrquez, editors, *Proceedings of the 57th Conference of the Association for Computational Linguistics, ACL 2019, Florence, Italy, July 28- August 2, 2019, Volume 1: Long Papers*, pages 5962–5971. Association for Computational Linguistics.

Devansh Jain and Luis Espinosa Anke. 2022. Distilling hypernymy relations from language models: On the effectiveness of zero-shot taxonomy induction. In Vivi Nastase, Ellie Pavlick, Mohammad Taher Pilehvar, José Camacho-Collados, and Alessandro Raganato, editors, *Proceedings of the 11th Joint Conference on Lexical and Computational Semantics, *SEM@NAACL-HLT 2022, Seattle, WA, USA, July 14-15, 2022*, pages 151–156. Association for Computational Linguistics.

Ziwei Ji, Nayeon Lee, Rita Frieske, Tiezheng Yu, Dan Su, Yan Xu, Etsuko Ishii, Yejin Bang, Andrea Madotto, and Pascale Fung. 2022. Survey of hallucination in natural language generation. *CoRR*, abs/2202.03629.

Zhengbao Jiang, Frank F. Xu, Jun Araki, and Graham Neubig. 2020. How can we know what language models know. *Trans. Assoc. Comput. Linguistics*, 8:423–438.

Xiang Lorraine Li, Adhiguna Kuncoro, Jordan Hoffmann, Cyprien de Masson d'Autume, Phil Blunsom, and Aida Nematzadeh. 2022. A systematic investigation of commonsense knowledge in large language models. In Yoav Goldberg, Zornitsa Kozareva, and Yue Zhang, editors, *Proceedings of the 2022 Conference on Empirical Methods in Natural Language Processing, EMNLP 2022, Abu Dhabi, United Arab Emirates, December 7-11, 2022*, pages 11838–11855. Association for Computational Linguistics.

Nelson F. Liu, Matt Gardner, Yonatan Belinkov, Matthew E. Peters, and Noah A. Smith. 2019. Linguistic knowledge and transferability of contextual representations. In Jill Burstein, Christy Doran, and Thamar Solorio, editors, *Proceedings of the 2019 Conference of the North American Chapter of the Association for Computational Linguistics: Human Language Technologies, NAACL-HLT 2019, Minneapolis, MN, USA, June 2-7, 2019, Volume 1 (Long and Short Papers)*, pages 1073–1094. Association for Computational Linguistics.

Weijie Liu, Peng Zhou, Zhe Zhao, Zhiruo Wang, Qi Ju, Haotang Deng, and Ping Wang. 2020. K-BERT: enabling language representation with knowledge graph. In *The Thirty-Fourth AAAI Conference on Artificial Intelligence, AAAI 2020, The Thirty-Second Innovative Applications of Artificial Intelligence Conference, IAAI 2020, The Tenth AAAI Symposium on Educational Advances in Artificial Intelligence, EAAI 2020, New York, NY, USA, February 7-12, 2020*, pages 2901–2908. AAAI Press.

Xiao Liu, Yanan Zheng, Zhengxiao Du, Ming Ding, Yujie Qian, Zhilin Yang, and Jie Tang. 2021a. GPT understands, too. *CoRR*, abs/2103.10385.

Ye Liu, Yao Wan, Lifang He, Hao Peng, and Philip S. Yu. 2021b. KG-BART: knowledge graph-augmented BART for generative commonsense reasoning. In *Thirty-Fifth AAAI Conference on Artificial Intelligence, AAAI 2021, Thirty-Third Conference on Innovative Applications of Artificial Intelligence, IAAI 2021, The Eleventh Symposium on Educational Advances in Artificial Intelligence, EAAI 2021, Virtual Event, February 2-9, 2021*, pages 6418–6425. AAAI Press.

Kevin Meng, David Bau, Alex Andonian, and Yonatan Belinkov. 2022a. Locating and editing factual knowledge in GPT. *CoRR*, abs/2202.05262.

Kevin Meng, Arnab Sen Sharma, Alex Andonian, Yonatan Belinkov, and David Bau. 2022b. Mass-editing memory in a transformer. *CoRR*, abs/2210.07229.

Eric Mitchell, Charles Lin, Antoine Bosselut, Chelsea Finn, and Christopher D. Manning. 2022. Fast model editing at scale. In *The Tenth International Conference on Learning Representations, ICLR 2022, Virtual Event, April 25-29, 2022*. OpenReview.net.

第二十二届中国计算语言学大会论文集，第1页-第8页，哈尔滨，中国，2023年8月3日至5日。

Reiichiro Nakano, Jacob Hilton, Suchir Balaji, Jeff Wu, Long Ouyang, Christina Kim, Christopher Hesse, Shantanu Jain, Vineet Kosaraju, William Saunders, Xu Jiang, Karl Cobbe, Tyna Eloundou, Gretchen Krueger, Kevin Button, Matthew Knight, Benjamin Chess, and John Schulman. 2021. Webgpt: Browser-assisted question-answering with human feedback. *CoRR*, abs/2112.09332.

Baolin Peng, Michel Galley, Pengcheng He, Hao Cheng, Yujia Xie, Yu Hu, Qiuyuan Huang, Lars Liden, Zhou Yu, Weizhu Chen, and Jianfeng Gao. 2023. Check your facts and try again: Improving large language models with external knowledge and automated feedback. *CoRR*, abs/2302.12813.

Matthew E. Peters, Mark Neumann, Robert L. Logan IV, Roy Schwartz, Vidur Joshi, Sameer Singh, and Noah A. Smith. 2019. Knowledge enhanced contextual word representations. In Kentaro Inui, Jing Jiang, Vincent Ng, and Xiaojun Wan, editors, *Proceedings of the 2019 Conference on Empirical Methods in Natural Language Processing and the 9th International Joint Conference on Natural Language Processing, EMNLP-IJCNLP 2019, Hong Kong, China, November 3-7, 2019*, pages 43–54. Association for Computational Linguistics.

Fabio Petroni, Tim Rocktäschel, Sebastian Riedel, Patrick S. H. Lewis, Anton Bakhtin, Yuxiang Wu, and Alexander H. Miller. 2019. Language models as knowledge bases? In Kentaro Inui, Jing Jiang, Vincent Ng, and Xiaojun Wan, editors, *Proceedings of the 2019 Conference on Empirical Methods in Natural Language Processing and the 9th International Joint Conference on Natural Language Processing, EMNLP-IJCNLP 2019, Hong Kong, China, November 3-7, 2019*, pages 2463–2473. Association for Computational Linguistics.

Anna Rogers, Olga Kovaleva, and Anna Rumshisky. 2020. A primer in bertology: What we know about how BERT works. *Trans. Assoc. Comput. Linguistics*, 8:842–866.

Corby Rosset, Chenyan Xiong, Minh Phan, Xia Song, Paul N. Bennett, and Saurabh Tiwary. 2020. Knowledge-aware language model pretraining. *CoRR*, abs/2007.00655.

Tara Safavi and Danai Koutra. 2021. Relational world knowledge representation in contextual language models: A review. In Marie-Francine Moens, Xuanjing Huang, Lucia Specia, and Scott Wen-tau Yih, editors, *Proceedings of the 2021 Conference on Empirical Methods in Natural Language Processing, EMNLP 2021, Virtual Event / Punta Cana, Dominican Republic, 7-11 November, 2021*, pages 1053–1067. Association for Computational Linguistics.

Tao Shen, Yi Mao, Pengcheng He, Guodong Long, Adam Trischler, and Weizhu Chen. 2020. Exploiting structured knowledge in text via graph-guided representation learning. In Bonnie Webber, Trevor Cohn, Yulan He, and Yang Liu, editors, *Proceedings of the 2020 Conference on Empirical Methods in Natural Language Processing, EMNLP 2020, Online, November 16-20, 2020*, pages 8980–8994. Association for Computational Linguistics.

Taylor Shin, Yasaman Razeghi, Robert L. Logan IV, Eric Wallace, and Sameer Singh. 2020. Autoprompt: Eliciting knowledge from language models with automatically generated prompts. In Bonnie Webber, Trevor Cohn, Yulan He, and Yang Liu, editors, *Proceedings of the 2020 Conference on Empirical Methods in Natural Language Processing, EMNLP 2020, Online, November 16-20, 2020*, pages 4222–4235. Association for Computational Linguistics.

Yu Sun, Shuohuan Wang, Yu-Kun Li, Shikun Feng, Xuyi Chen, Han Zhang, Xin Tian, Danxiang Zhu, Hao Tian, and Hua Wu. 2019. ERNIE: enhanced representation through knowledge integration. *CoRR*, abs/1904.09223.

Tianxiang Sun, Yunfan Shao, Xipeng Qiu, Qipeng Guo, Yaru Hu, Xuanjing Huang, and Zheng Zhang. 2020. Colake: Contextualized language and knowledge embedding. In Donia Scott, Núria Bel, and Chengqing Zong, editors, *Proceedings of the 28th International Conference on Computational Linguistics, COLING 2020, Barcelona, Spain (Online), December 8-13, 2020*, pages 3660–3670. International Committee on Computational Linguistics.

Yu Sun, Shuohuan Wang, Shikun Feng, Siyu Ding, Chao Pang, Junyuan Shang, Jiaxiang Liu, Xuyi Chen, Yanbin Zhao, Yuxiang Lu, Weixin Liu, Zhihua Wu, Weibao Gong, Jianzhong Liang, Zhizhou Shang, Peng Sun, Wei Liu, Xuan Ouyang, Dianhai Yu, Hao Tian, Hua Wu, and Haifeng Wang. 2021. ERNIE 3.0: Large-scale knowledge enhanced pre-training for language understanding and generation. *CoRR*, abs/2107.02137.

Chenhao Wang, Yubo Chen, Zhipeng Xue, Yang Zhou, and Jun Zhao. 2021a. Cognet: Bridging linguistic knowledge, world knowledge and commonsense knowledge. In *Thirty-Fifth AAAI Conference on Artificial Intelligence, AAAI 2021, Thirty-Third Conference on Innovative Applications of Artificial*

第二十二届中国计算语言学大会论文集，第1页-第8页，哈尔滨，中国，2023年8月3日至5日。

Intelligence, IAAI 2021, The Eleventh Symposium on Educational Advances in Artificial Intelligence, EAAI 2021, Virtual Event, February 2-9, 2021, pages 16114–16116. AAAI Press.

Ruize Wang, Duyu Tang, Nan Duan, Zhongyu Wei, Xuanjing Huang, Jianshu Ji, Guihong Cao, Daxin Jiang, and Ming Zhou. 2021b. K-adapter: Infusing knowledge into pre-trained models with adapters. In Chengqing Zong, Fei Xia, Wenjie Li, and Roberto Navigli, editors, *Findings of the Association for Computational Linguistics: ACL/IJCNLP 2021, Online Event, August 1-6, 2021*, volume ACL/IJCNLP 2021 of *Findings of ACL*, pages 1405–1418. Association for Computational Linguistics.

Xiaozhi Wang, Tianyu Gao, Zhaocheng Zhu, Zhengyan Zhang, Zhiyuan Liu, Juanzi Li, and Jian Tang. 2021c. KEPLER: A unified model for knowledge embedding and pre-trained language representation. *Trans. Assoc. Comput. Linguistics*, 9:176–194.

Chenhao Wang, Jiachun Li, Yubo Chen, Kang Liu, and Jun Zhao. 2022. Cn-automic: Distilling chinese commonsense knowledge from pretrained language models. In Yoav Goldberg, Zornitsa Kozareva, and Yue Zhang, editors, *Proceedings of the 2022 Conference on Empirical Methods in Natural Language Processing, EMNLP 2022, Abu Dhabi, United Arab Emirates, December 7-11, 2022*, pages 9253–9265. Association for Computational Linguistics.

Yuqi Wang, Wei Wang, Qi Chen, Kaizhu Huang, Anh Nguyen, Suparna De, and Amir Hussain. 2023. Fusing external knowledge resources for natural language understanding techniques: A survey. *Inf. Fusion*, 92:190–204.

Peter West, Chandra Bhagavatula, Jack Hessel, Jena D. Hwang, Liwei Jiang, Ronan Le Bras, Ximing Lu, Sean Welleck, and Yejin Choi. 2022. Symbolic knowledge distillation: from general language models to commonsense models. In Marine Carpuat, Marie-Catherine de Marneffe, and Iván Vladimir Meza Ruíz, editors, *Proceedings of the 2022 Conference of the North American Chapter of the Association for Computational Linguistics: Human Language Technologies, NAACL 2022, Seattle, WA, United States, July 10-15, 2022*, pages 4602–4625. Association for Computational Linguistics.

Da Yin, Li Dong, Hao Cheng, Xiaodong Liu, Kai-Wei Chang, Furu Wei, and Jianfeng Gao. 2022. A survey of knowledge-intensive NLP with pre-trained language models. *CoRR*, abs/2202.08772.

Zhengyan Zhang, Xu Han, Zhiyuan Liu, Xin Jiang, Maosong Sun, and Qun Liu. 2019. ERNIE: enhanced language representation with informative entities. In Anna Korhonen, David R. Traum, and Lluís Màrquez, editors, *Proceedings of the 57th Conference of the Association for Computational Linguistics, ACL 2019, Florence, Italy, July 28- August 2, 2019, Volume 1: Long Papers*, pages 1441–1451. Association for Computational Linguistics.

Xuhui Zhou, Yue Zhang, Leyang Cui, and Dandan Huang. 2020. Evaluating commonsense in pre-trained language models. In *The Thirty-Fourth AAAI Conference on Artificial Intelligence, AAAI 2020, The Thirty-Second Innovative Applications of Artificial Intelligence Conference, IAAI 2020, The Tenth AAAI Symposium on Educational Advances in Artificial Intelligence, EAAI 2020, New York, NY, USA, February 7-12, 2020*, pages 9733–9740. AAAI Press.

第二十二届中国计算语言学大会论文集，第1页-第8页，哈尔滨，中国，2023年8月3日至5日。

Safety and Ethical Concerns of Large Language Models

Zhiheng Xi, Rui Zheng, Tao Gui
School of Computer Science, Fudan University, Shanghai, China
Institute of Modern Languages and Linguistics, Fudan University, Shanghai, China
Shanghai Key Laboratory of Intelligent Information Processing, Shanghai, China
zhxi22@m.fudan.edu.cn, {rzheng20,tgui}@fudan.edu.cn

Abstract

Recent months have witnessed significant progress in the field of large language models (LLMs). Represented by ChatGPT and GPT-4, LLMs perform well in various natural language processing tasks and have been applied to many downstream applications to facilitate people's lives. However, there still exist safety and ethical concerns. Specifically, LLMs suffer from social bias, robustness problems, and poisoning issues, all of which may induce LLMs to spew harmful contents. We propose this tutorial as a gentle introduction to the safety and ethical issues of LLMs.

1 Introduction

As the model size and dataset size scale up in recent natural language processing field, large language models like ChatGPT and GPT-4 have exhibited exceptional performance in a variety of NLP tasks and can even perform complex reasoning or in-context learning (i.e., generalizing to a new task from a few examples) (Brown et al., 2020; Ouyang et al., 2022; OpenAI, 2023; Wei et al., 2022). Moreover, many downstream applications have been developed based on LLMs, which brings significant benefits and convenience to people (Schick et al., 2023; Driess et al., 2023). Despite their fantastic capabilities and potentials, LLMs have raised valid concerns regarding their safety and ethical implications (Bommasani et al., 2021). To be specific, LLMs suffer from social bias (Ferrara, 2023), robustness problems (Zhuo et al., 2023; Wang et al., 2023; Chen et al., 2023), and poisoning issues(Chen et al., 2021), all of which may lead LLMs to generate harmful and rude contents. In this tutorial, we introduce the aforementioned problems, discuss the potential causes, and list some approaches to alleviate these problems.

2 Bias

Language models pre-trained on large-scale corpus usually demonstrate various types of biases like racial discrimination and gender discrimination (Basta et al., 2019; Beltagy et al., 2019; Kurita et al., 2019; Zhang et al., 2020). We follow Bender et al. (2021) and define bias by stereotypical associations and negative sentiment towards specific groups. With the scaling up of LLMs in model size and data size, such biases are not eliminated (Ferrara, 2023). Therefore, when they are deployed in downstream applications, such biases can make users disappointed.

The question of why (large) language models are prone to bias has been well explored, and most of the works suggest that the biases are a reflection of training data patterns (Henderson et al., 2018; Hutchinson et al., 2020; Tan and Celis, 2019; Guo and Caliskan, 2021). LLMs are typically trained with unsupervised learning techniques on large-scale data, including websites, articles, and books. The data may contain unfair or biased characteristics. For example, Hutchinson et al. (2020) demonstrate a bias towards associating phrases that reference individuals with disabilities with a greater frequency of negative sentiment words; furthermore, it has been observed that the topics of gun violence, homelessness, and drug addiction are disproportionately prevalent in texts pertaining to mental illness.

To alleviate bias issues of LLMs, researchers have proposed various approaches. A line of work tries to identify the sources that are most responsible for biases and take actions to make models obviate

Proceedings of the 22nd China National Conference on Computational Linguistics, pages 9-16, Harbin, China, August 3 - 5, 2023.

reflecting the inequities or biases (Bommasani et al., 2021; Lu et al., 2020; Zhao et al., 2018). Some other work develops calibrating techniques to address bias problems of LLMs (Zhao et al., 2021; Holtzman et al., 2021). Another potential direction is to leverage alignment techniques like Reinforcement Learning from Human Feedback (RLHF) (Bai et al., 2022; Ouyang et al., 2022; Ferrara, 2023; Zheng et al., 2023), where LLMs are trained to align with human values and thus some biases can be mitigated.

Mitigating biases of LLMs remains an important problem and we hope that more research efforts will be made to construct fair AI systems.

3 Robustness

Pretrained language models are known to be vulnerable to adversarial instances crafted by performing subtle perturbations on normal ones (Ren et al., 2019; Garg and Ramakrishnan, 2020; Wang et al., 2021b). With increasing scales, LLMs still face such challenges and their performance suffers significant drops under adversarial attacks (Zhuo et al., 2023; Wang et al., 2023; Chen et al., 2023). For example, when conducting in-context learning, models' performance can be unstable when changing the choice of prompt format, training examples and the order of examples (Chen et al., 2022; Zhao et al., 2021).

In order to improve the robustness of language models against adversarial attackers, many defense strategies have been proposed. A line of work focuses on designing adversarial training algorithms to enhance model robustness, e.g., FreeLB (Zhu et al., 2020) and InfoBERT (Wang et al., 2021a). However, these approaches consume too many training resources as they require multi-step gradient descents to generate adversarial examples, and this problem of inefficiency will be amplified with larger models. Another line of work searches for a robust model architecture with sparse optimization techniques (Xi et al., 2022; Zheng et al., 2022). However, such techniques may induce a trade-off between robustness and accuracy (Zhang et al., 2019; Tsipras et al., 2019). Some other work tries to design prompts to elicit reliable and robust responses from LLMs (Si et al., 2022), which is a potential direction as prompt engineering does not require training models or changing their architectures.

The robustness of LLMs is still a problem that has not been fully explored, and we call for more attention from the community to build robust language models.

4 Poisoning

In an ICML 2017 outstanding paper (Koh and Liang, 2017), the authors employ the novel Influence Function to gauge alterations in model parameters, could provide a quantitative evaluation of the impact individual training samples on the model. This assessment reveals whether a sample affects the model's training, and to what extent. Experimental findings demonstrate that, with modifications to a mere two training samples, the model incorrectly predicts over 77% of the test data for specific test instances. Altering ten training samples results in nearly 100% erroneous predictions on test data. Gu et al. (2017) cleverly introduce poisoned data into the training set, ensuring that the model's accuracy on pristine data remains constant or marginally declines, while simultaneously triggering specific outputs when presented with data containing particular trigger words. Such poisoned models may be elicited to generate toxic contents like abusive language, hate speech, violent speech (Liang et al., 2022; Gururangan et al., 2022).

Dai et al. (2019) select brief sentences as backdoor triggers, such as "I watched this 3D movie," and randomly incorporate them into movie reviews to generate tainted samples for backdoor training. Kurita et al. (2020) employ rare and nonsensical words like "cf" as triggers. Similarly, Chen et al. (2021) utilize words as triggers, experimenting with words of varying frequencies. Chen and Dai (2021) postulate that triggers associate with specific neurons, influencing only certain hidden states. Qi et al. (2021) suggest a defense premised on the observation that perplexity undergoes significant alterations when trigger words are excised from samples. Li et al. (2021) conduct a thorough analysis of backdoor attacks in text classification, ultimately developing a backdoor-free text classifier training framework, dubbed BFClass.

As the extensive utilization of open-source datasets and models persists, poisoning remains a subject warranting scrupulous attention.

Proceedings of the 22nd China National Conference on Computational Linguistics, pages 9-16, Harbin, China, August 3 - 5, 2023.

5 Tutorial Outline

Part I: Introduction (20 min)

- The development of large language models
- The importance of safety and ethical concerns
- Safety and ethical concerns LLMs suffer
  - Social bias
  - Robustness problems
  - Poisoning issues

Part II: Bias (20 min)

- Definition, types and sources of Bias
- Bias of large language models
- Methods to alleviate bias issues
  - Identify the causes of bias and addressing them
  - Calibrating methods
  - Reinforcement Learning from Human Feedback

Part III: Robustness (20 min)

- Textual adversarial robustness
- Robustness of large language models
- Defense strategies to improve robustness
  - Adversarial training
  - Finding robust structures of neural networks
  - Prompting methods

Part IV: Poisoning (20 min)

- Definition of poisoning issues
- Poisoning methods
  - Dataset attacks
  - Backdoors and triggers

Part V: Conclusion (10 min)

6 Reading List

1. On the Opportunities and Risks of Foundation Models (Bommasani et al., 2021);
2. Ethical challenges in data-driven dialogue systems (Henderson et al., 2018);
3. Training a helpful and harmless assistant with reinforcement learning from human feedback (Bai et al., 2022);
4. Training language models to follow instructions with human feedback (Ouyang et al., 2022);
5. On the dangers of stochastic parrots: Can language models be too big?(Bender et al., 2021)
6. Should chatgpt be biased? challenges and risks of bias in large language models (Ferrara, 2023);

Proceedings of the 22nd China National Conference on Computational Linguistics, pages 9-16, Harbin, China, August 3 - 5, 2023.

7. Detecting emergent intersectional biases: Contextualized word embeddings contain a distribution of human-like biases (Guo and Caliskan, 2021);

8. How robust is GPT-3.5 to predecessors? A comprehensive study on language understanding tasks (Chen et al., 2023);

9. Badnets: Identifying vulnerabilities in the machine learning model supply chain (Gu et al., 2017);

10. Secrets of RLHF in Large Language Models Part I: PPO (Zheng et al., 2023);

7 Instructors

Tao Gui is an associate professor at the Institute of Modern Languages and Linguistics of Fudan University. He is the key member of the FudanNLP group[0]. He is a member of ACL, a member of the Youth Working Committee of the Chinese Information Processing Society of China, and the member of the Language and Knowledge Computing Professional Committee of the Chinese Information Processing Society of China. He has published more than 40 papers in top international academic conferences and journals such as ACL, ENNLP, AAAI, IJCAI, SIGIR, and so on. He has served as area chair or PCs for SIGIR, AAAI, IJCAI, TPAMI, and ARR. He has received the Outstanding Doctoral Dissertation Award of the Chinese Information Processing Society of China, the area chair favorite Award of COLING 2018, the outstanding Paper Award of NLPCC 2019, a scholar of young talent promoting projects of CAST, and the Shanghai Rising-Star Program.

Homepage: `https://guitaowufeng.github.io`

Rui Zheng is a Ph.D. student in the class of 2020 at the School of Computer Science, Fudan University, is supervised by Professor Zhang Qi. His research interests include robust models, dataset debiasing, and large model alignment. He has participated in the development of the large-scale robustness detection tool TextFlint and has published multiple first-author/co-first-author papers at conferences such as ACL, EMNLP, and COLING.

Zhiheng Xi is a first-year master student the School of Computer Science, Fudan University. Prior to that, he received his bachelor's degree from Nanjing University. His research interests lie in robust machine learning, sparse neural networks, prompting techniques, and complex reasoning ability of LLMs. He has published multiple first-author/co-first-author papers at EMNLP and ACL.

References

Yuntao Bai, Andy Jones, Kamal Ndousse, Amanda Askell, Anna Chen, Nova DasSarma, Dawn Drain, Stanislav Fort, Deep Ganguli, Tom Henighan, Nicholas Joseph, Saurav Kadavath, Jackson Kernion, Tom Conerly, Sheer El Showk, Nelson Elhage, Zac Hatfield-Dodds, Danny Hernandez, Tristan Hume, Scott Johnston, Shauna Kravec, Liane Lovitt, Neel Nanda, Catherine Olsson, Dario Amodei, Tom B. Brown, Jack Clark, Sam McCandlish, Chris Olah, Benjamin Mann, and Jared Kaplan. 2022. Training a helpful and harmless assistant with reinforcement learning from human feedback. *CoRR*, abs/2204.05862.

Christine Basta, Marta Ruiz Costa-jussà, and Noe Casas. 2019. Evaluating the underlying gender bias in contextualized word embeddings. *CoRR*, abs/1904.08783.

Iz Beltagy, Kyle Lo, and Arman Cohan. 2019. Scibert: A pretrained language model for scientific text. In Kentaro Inui, Jing Jiang, Vincent Ng, and Xiaojun Wan, editors, *Proceedings of the 2019 Conference on Empirical Methods in Natural Language Processing and the 9th International Joint Conference on Natural Language Processing, EMNLP-IJCNLP 2019, Hong Kong, China, November 3-7, 2019*, pages 3613–3618. Association for Computational Linguistics.

Emily M. Bender, Timnit Gebru, Angelina McMillan-Major, and Shmargaret Shmitchell. 2021. On the dangers of stochastic parrots: Can language models be too big? In Madeleine Clare Elish, William Isaac, and Richard S. Zemel, editors, *FAccT '21: 2021 ACM Conference on Fairness, Accountability, and Transparency, Virtual Event / Toronto, Canada, March 3-10, 2021*, pages 610–623. ACM.

[0] `https://nlp.fudan.edu.cn`

Proceedings of the 22nd China National Conference on Computational Linguistics, pages 9-16, Harbin, China, August 3 - 5, 2023.

Rishi Bommasani, Drew A. Hudson, Ehsan Adeli, Russ B. Altman, Simran Arora, Sydney von Arx, Michael S. Bernstein, Jeannette Bohg, Antoine Bosselut, Emma Brunskill, Erik Brynjolfsson, Shyamal Buch, Dallas Card, Rodrigo Castellon, Niladri S. Chatterji, Annie S. Chen, Kathleen Creel, Jared Quincy Davis, Dorottya Demszky, Chris Donahue, Moussa Doumbouya, Esin Durmus, Stefano Ermon, John Etchemendy, Kawin Ethayarajh, Li Fei-Fei, Chelsea Finn, Trevor Gale, Lauren Gillespie, Karan Goel, Noah D. Goodman, Shelby Grossman, Neel Guha, Tatsunori Hashimoto, Peter Henderson, John Hewitt, Daniel E. Ho, Jenny Hong, Kyle Hsu, Jing Huang, Thomas Icard, Saahil Jain, Dan Jurafsky, Pratyusha Kalluri, Siddharth Karamcheti, Geoff Keeling, Fereshte Khani, Omar Khattab, Pang Wei Koh, Mark S. Krass, Ranjay Krishna, Rohith Kuditipudi, and et al. 2021. On the opportunities and risks of foundation models. *CoRR*, abs/2108.07258.

Tom B. Brown, Benjamin Mann, Nick Ryder, Melanie Subbiah, Jared Kaplan, Prafulla Dhariwal, Arvind Neelakantan, Pranav Shyam, Girish Sastry, Amanda Askell, Sandhini Agarwal, Ariel Herbert-Voss, Gretchen Krueger, Tom Henighan, Rewon Child, Aditya Ramesh, Daniel M. Ziegler, Jeffrey Wu, Clemens Winter, Christopher Hesse, Mark Chen, Eric Sigler, Mateusz Litwin, Scott Gray, Benjamin Chess, Jack Clark, Christopher Berner, Sam McCandlish, Alec Radford, Ilya Sutskever, and Dario Amodei. 2020. Language models are few-shot learners. In Hugo Larochelle, Marc'Aurelio Ranzato, Raia Hadsell, Maria-Florina Balcan, and Hsuan-Tien Lin, editors, *Advances in Neural Information Processing Systems 33: Annual Conference on Neural Information Processing Systems 2020, NeurIPS 2020, December 6-12, 2020, virtual.*

Chuanshuai Chen and Jiazhu Dai. 2021. Mitigating backdoor attacks in lstm-based text classification systems by backdoor keyword identification. *Neurocomputing*, 452:253–262.

Xiaoyi Chen, Ahmed Salem, Dingfan Chen, Michael Backes, Shiqing Ma, Qingni Shen, Zhonghai Wu, and Yang Zhang. 2021. Badnl: Backdoor attacks against NLP models with semantic-preserving improvements. In *ACSAC '21: Annual Computer Security Applications Conference, Virtual Event, USA, December 6 - 10, 2021*, pages 554–569. ACM.

Yanda Chen, Chen Zhao, Zhou Yu, Kathleen R. McKeown, and He He. 2022. On the relation between sensitivity and accuracy in in-context learning. *CoRR*, abs/2209.07661.

Xuanting Chen, Junjie Ye, Can Zu, Nuo Xu, Rui Zheng, Minlong Peng, Jie Zhou, Tao Gui, Qi Zhang, and Xuanjing Huang. 2023. How robust is GPT-3.5 to predecessors? A comprehensive study on language understanding tasks. *CoRR*, abs/2303.00293.

Jiazhu Dai, Chuanshuai Chen, and Yufeng Li. 2019. A backdoor attack against lstm-based text classification systems. *IEEE Access*, 7:138872–138878.

Danny Driess, Fei Xia, Mehdi S. M. Sajjadi, Corey Lynch, Aakanksha Chowdhery, Brian Ichter, Ayzaan Wahid, Jonathan Tompson, Quan Vuong, Tianhe Yu, Wenlong Huang, Yevgen Chebotar, Pierre Sermanet, Daniel Duckworth, Sergey Levine, Vincent Vanhoucke, Karol Hausman, Marc Toussaint, Klaus Greff, Andy Zeng, Igor Mordatch, and Pete Florence. 2023. Palm-e: An embodied multimodal language model. *CoRR*, abs/2303.03378.

Emilio Ferrara. 2023. Should chatgpt be biased? challenges and risks of bias in large language models. *CoRR*, abs/2304.03738.

Siddhant Garg and Goutham Ramakrishnan. 2020. BAE: bert-based adversarial examples for text classification. In Bonnie Webber, Trevor Cohn, Yulan He, and Yang Liu, editors, *Proceedings of the 2020 Conference on Empirical Methods in Natural Language Processing, EMNLP 2020, Online, November 16-20, 2020*, pages 6174–6181. Association for Computational Linguistics.

Tianyu Gu, Brendan Dolan-Gavitt, and Siddharth Garg. 2017. Badnets: Identifying vulnerabilities in the machine learning model supply chain. *CoRR*, abs/1708.06733.

Wei Guo and Aylin Caliskan. 2021. Detecting emergent intersectional biases: Contextualized word embeddings contain a distribution of human-like biases. In Marion Fourcade, Benjamin Kuipers, Seth Lazar, and Deirdre K. Mulligan, editors, *AIES '21: AAAI/ACM Conference on AI, Ethics, and Society, Virtual Event, USA, May 19-21, 2021*, pages 122–133. ACM.

Suchin Gururangan, Dallas Card, Sarah K. Dreier, Emily K. Gade, Leroy Z. Wang, Zeyu Wang, Luke Zettlemoyer, and Noah A. Smith. 2022. Whose language counts as high quality? measuring language ideologies in text data selection. In Yoav Goldberg, Zornitsa Kozareva, and Yue Zhang, editors, *Proceedings of the 2022 Conference on Empirical Methods in Natural Language Processing, EMNLP 2022, Abu Dhabi, United Arab Emirates, December 7-11, 2022*, pages 2562–2580. Association for Computational Linguistics.

Proceedings of the 22nd China National Conference on Computational Linguistics, pages 9-16, Harbin, China, August 3 - 5, 2023.

Peter Henderson, Koustuv Sinha, Nicolas Angelard-Gontier, Nan Rosemary Ke, Genevieve Fried, Ryan Lowe, and Joelle Pineau. 2018. Ethical challenges in data-driven dialogue systems. In Jason Furman, Gary E. Marchant, Huw Price, and Francesca Rossi, editors, *Proceedings of the 2018 AAAI/ACM Conference on AI, Ethics, and Society, AIES 2018, New Orleans, LA, USA, February 02-03, 2018*, pages 123–129. ACM.

Ari Holtzman, Peter West, Vered Shwartz, Yejin Choi, and Luke Zettlemoyer. 2021. Surface form competition: Why the highest probability answer isn't always right. In Marie-Francine Moens, Xuanjing Huang, Lucia Specia, and Scott Wen-tau Yih, editors, *Proceedings of the 2021 Conference on Empirical Methods in Natural Language Processing, EMNLP 2021, Virtual Event / Punta Cana, Dominican Republic, 7-11 November, 2021*, pages 7038–7051. Association for Computational Linguistics.

Ben Hutchinson, Vinodkumar Prabhakaran, Emily Denton, Kellie Webster, Yu Zhong, and Stephen Denuyl. 2020. Social biases in NLP models as barriers for persons with disabilities. In Dan Jurafsky, Joyce Chai, Natalie Schluter, and Joel R. Tetreault, editors, *Proceedings of the 58th Annual Meeting of the Association for Computational Linguistics, ACL 2020, Online, July 5-10, 2020*, pages 5491–5501. Association for Computational Linguistics.

Pang Wei Koh and Percy Liang. 2017. Understanding black-box predictions via influence functions. In Doina Precup and Yee Whye Teh, editors, *Proceedings of the 34th International Conference on Machine Learning, ICML 2017, Sydney, NSW, Australia, 6-11 August 2017*, volume 70 of *Proceedings of Machine Learning Research*, pages 1885–1894. PMLR.

Keita Kurita, Nidhi Vyas, Ayush Pareek, Alan W. Black, and Yulia Tsvetkov. 2019. Measuring bias in contextualized word representations. *CoRR*, abs/1906.07337.

Keita Kurita, Paul Michel, and Graham Neubig. 2020. Weight poisoning attacks on pre-trained models. *CoRR*, abs/2004.06660.

Zichao Li, Dheeraj Mekala, Chengyu Dong, and Jingbo Shang. 2021. Bfclass: A backdoor-free text classification framework. In Marie-Francine Moens, Xuanjing Huang, Lucia Specia, and Scott Wen-tau Yih, editors, *Findings of the Association for Computational Linguistics: EMNLP 2021, Virtual Event / Punta Cana, Dominican Republic, 16-20 November, 2021*, pages 444–453. Association for Computational Linguistics.

Percy Liang, Rishi Bommasani, Tony Lee, Dimitris Tsipras, Dilara Soylu, Michihiro Yasunaga, Yian Zhang, Deepak Narayanan, Yuhuai Wu, Ananya Kumar, Benjamin Newman, Binhang Yuan, Bobby Yan, Ce Zhang, Christian Cosgrove, Christopher D. Manning, Christopher Ré, Diana Acosta-Navas, Drew A. Hudson, Eric Zelikman, Esin Durmus, Faisal Ladhak, Frieda Rong, Hongyu Ren, Huaxiu Yao, Jue Wang, Keshav Santhanam, Laurel J. Orr, Lucia Zheng, Mert Yüksekgönül, Mirac Suzgun, Nathan Kim, Neel Guha, Niladri S. Chatterji, Omar Khattab, Peter Henderson, Qian Huang, Ryan Chi, Sang Michael Xie, Shibani Santurkar, Surya Ganguli, Tatsunori Hashimoto, Thomas Icard, Tianyi Zhang, Vishrav Chaudhary, William Wang, Xuechen Li, Yifan Mai, Yuhui Zhang, and Yuta Koreeda. 2022. Holistic evaluation of language models. *CoRR*, abs/2211.09110.

Kaiji Lu, Piotr Mardziel, Fangjing Wu, Preetam Amancharla, and Anupam Datta. 2020. Gender bias in neural natural language processing. In Vivek Nigam, Tajana Ban Kirigin, Carolyn L. Talcott, Joshua D. Guttman, Stepan L. Kuznetsov, Boon Thau Loo, and Mitsuhiro Okada, editors, *Logic, Language, and Security - Essays Dedicated to Andre Scedrov on the Occasion of His 65th Birthday*, volume 12300 of *Lecture Notes in Computer Science*, pages 189–202. Springer.

OpenAI. 2023. GPT-4 technical report. *CoRR*, abs/2303.08774.

Long Ouyang, Jeff Wu, Xu Jiang, Diogo Almeida, Carroll L. Wainwright, Pamela Mishkin, Chong Zhang, Sandhini Agarwal, Katarina Slama, Alex Ray, John Schulman, Jacob Hilton, Fraser Kelton, Luke Miller, Maddie Simens, Amanda Askell, Peter Welinder, Paul F. Christiano, Jan Leike, and Ryan Lowe. 2022. Training language models to follow instructions with human feedback. *CoRR*, abs/2203.02155.

Fanchao Qi, Yangyi Chen, Mukai Li, Yuan Yao, Zhiyuan Liu, and Maosong Sun. 2021. ONION: A simple and effective defense against textual backdoor attacks. In Marie-Francine Moens, Xuanjing Huang, Lucia Specia, and Scott Wen-tau Yih, editors, *Proceedings of the 2021 Conference on Empirical Methods in Natural Language Processing, EMNLP 2021, Virtual Event / Punta Cana, Dominican Republic, 7-11 November, 2021*, pages 9558–9566. Association for Computational Linguistics.

Shuhuai Ren, Yihe Deng, Kun He, and Wanxiang Che. 2019. Generating natural language adversarial examples through probability weighted word saliency. In Anna Korhonen, David R. Traum, and Lluís Màrquez, editors, *Proceedings of the 57th Conference of the Association for Computational Linguistics, ACL 2019, Florence, Italy, July 28- August 2, 2019, Volume 1: Long Papers*, pages 1085–1097. Association for Computational Linguistics.

Proceedings of the 22nd China National Conference on Computational Linguistics, pages 9-16, Harbin, China, August 3 - 5, 2023.

Timo Schick, Jane Dwivedi-Yu, Roberto Dessì, Roberta Raileanu, Maria Lomeli, Luke Zettlemoyer, Nicola Cancedda, and Thomas Scialom. 2023. Toolformer: Language models can teach themselves to use tools. *CoRR*, abs/2302.04761.

Chenglei Si, Zhe Gan, Zhengyuan Yang, Shuohang Wang, Jianfeng Wang, Jordan L. Boyd-Graber, and Lijuan Wang. 2022. Prompting GPT-3 to be reliable. *CoRR*, abs/2210.09150.

Yi Chern Tan and L. Elisa Celis. 2019. Assessing social and intersectional biases in contextualized word representations. In Hanna M. Wallach, Hugo Larochelle, Alina Beygelzimer, Florence d'Alché-Buc, Emily B. Fox, and Roman Garnett, editors, *Advances in Neural Information Processing Systems 32: Annual Conference on Neural Information Processing Systems 2019, NeurIPS 2019, December 8-14, 2019, Vancouver, BC, Canada*, pages 13209–13220.

Dimitris Tsipras, Shibani Santurkar, Logan Engstrom, Alexander Turner, and Aleksander Madry. 2019. Robustness may be at odds with accuracy. In *7th International Conference on Learning Representations, ICLR 2019, New Orleans, LA, USA, May 6-9, 2019*. OpenReview.net.

Boxin Wang, Shuohang Wang, Yu Cheng, Zhe Gan, Ruoxi Jia, Bo Li, and Jingjing Liu. 2021a. Infobert: Improving robustness of language models from an information theoretic perspective. In *9th International Conference on Learning Representations, ICLR 2021, Virtual Event, Austria, May 3-7, 2021*. OpenReview.net.

Xiao Wang, Qin Liu, Tao Gui, Qi Zhang, Yicheng Zou, Xin Zhou, Jiacheng Ye, Yongxin Zhang, Rui Zheng, Zexiong Pang, Qinzhuo Wu, Zhengyan Li, Chong Zhang, Ruotian Ma, Zichu Fei, Ruijian Cai, Jun Zhao, Xingwu Hu, Zhiheng Yan, Yiding Tan, Yuan Hu, Qiyuan Bian, Zhihua Liu, Shan Qin, Bolin Zhu, Xiaoyu Xing, Jinlan Fu, Yue Zhang, Minlong Peng, Xiaoqing Zheng, Yaqian Zhou, Zhongyu Wei, Xipeng Qiu, and Xuanjing Huang. 2021b. Textflint: Unified multilingual robustness evaluation toolkit for natural language processing. In Heng Ji, Jong C. Park, and Rui Xia, editors, *Proceedings of the Joint Conference of the 59th Annual Meeting of the Association for Computational Linguistics and the 11th International Joint Conference on Natural Language Processing, ACL 2021 - System Demonstrations, Online, August 1-6, 2021*, pages 347–355. Association for Computational Linguistics.

Jindong Wang, Xixu Hu, Wenxin Hou, Hao Chen, Runkai Zheng, Yidong Wang, Linyi Yang, Haojun Huang, Wei Ye, Xiubo Geng, Binxing Jiao, Yue Zhang, and Xing Xie. 2023. On the robustness of chatgpt: An adversarial and out-of-distribution perspective. *CoRR*, abs/2302.12095.

Jason Wei, Xuezhi Wang, Dale Schuurmans, Maarten Bosma, Ed H. Chi, Quoc Le, and Denny Zhou. 2022. Chain of thought prompting elicits reasoning in large language models. *CoRR*, abs/2201.11903.

Zhiheng Xi, Rui Zheng, Tao Gui, Qi Zhang, and Xuanjing Huang. 2022. Efficient adversarial training with robust early-bird tickets. In Yoav Goldberg, Zornitsa Kozareva, and Yue Zhang, editors, *Proceedings of the 2022 Conference on Empirical Methods in Natural Language Processing, EMNLP 2022, Abu Dhabi, United Arab Emirates, December 7-11, 2022*, pages 8318–8331. Association for Computational Linguistics.

Hongyang Zhang, Yaodong Yu, Jiantao Jiao, Eric P. Xing, Laurent El Ghaoui, and Michael I. Jordan. 2019. Theoretically principled trade-off between robustness and accuracy. In Kamalika Chaudhuri and Ruslan Salakhutdinov, editors, *Proceedings of the 36th International Conference on Machine Learning, ICML 2019, 9-15 June 2019, Long Beach, California, USA*, volume 97 of *Proceedings of Machine Learning Research*, pages 7472–7482. PMLR.

Haoran Zhang, Amy X. Lu, Mohamed Abdalla, Matthew B. A. McDermott, and Marzyeh Ghassemi. 2020. Hurtful words: quantifying biases in clinical contextual word embeddings. In Marzyeh Ghassemi, editor, *ACM CHIL '20: ACM Conference on Health, Inference, and Learning, Toronto, Ontario, Canada, April 2-4, 2020 [delayed]*, pages 110–120. ACM.

Jieyu Zhao, Yichao Zhou, Zeyu Li, Wei Wang, and Kai-Wei Chang. 2018. Learning gender-neutral word embeddings. In Ellen Riloff, David Chiang, Julia Hockenmaier, and Jun'ichi Tsujii, editors, *Proceedings of the 2018 Conference on Empirical Methods in Natural Language Processing, Brussels, Belgium, October 31 - November 4, 2018*, pages 4847–4853. Association for Computational Linguistics.

Zihao Zhao, Eric Wallace, Shi Feng, Dan Klein, and Sameer Singh. 2021. Calibrate before use: Improving few-shot performance of language models. In Marina Meila and Tong Zhang, editors, *Proceedings of the 38th International Conference on Machine Learning, ICML 2021, 18-24 July 2021, Virtual Event*, volume 139 of *Proceedings of Machine Learning Research*, pages 12697–12706. PMLR.

Proceedings of the 22nd China National Conference on Computational Linguistics, pages 9-16, Harbin, China, August 3 - 5, 2023.

Rui Zheng, Bao Rong, Yuhao Zhou, Di Liang, Sirui Wang, Wei Wu, Tao Gui, Qi Zhang, and Xuanjing Huang. 2022. Robust lottery tickets for pre-trained language models. In Smaranda Muresan, Preslav Nakov, and Aline Villavicencio, editors, *Proceedings of the 60th Annual Meeting of the Association for Computational Linguistics (Volume 1: Long Papers), ACL 2022, Dublin, Ireland, May 22-27, 2022*, pages 2211–2224. Association for Computational Linguistics.

Rui Zheng, Shihan Dou, Songyang Gao, Yuan Hua, Wei Shen, Binghai Wang, Yan Liu, Senjie Jin, Qin Liu, Yuhao Zhou, Limao Xiong, Lu Chen, Zhiheng Xi, Nuo Xu, Wenbin Lai, Minghao Zhu, Cheng Chang, Zhangyue Yin, Rongxiang Weng, Wensen Cheng, Haoran Huang, Tianxiang Sun, Hang Yan, Tao Gui, Qi Zhang, Xipeng Qiu, and Xuanjing Huang. 2023. Secrets of rlhf in large language models part i: Ppo. *arXiv preprint arXiv:2307.04964*.

Chen Zhu, Yu Cheng, Zhe Gan, Siqi Sun, Tom Goldstein, and Jingjing Liu. 2020. Freelb: Enhanced adversarial training for natural language understanding. In *8th International Conference on Learning Representations, ICLR 2020, Addis Ababa, Ethiopia, April 26-30, 2020*. OpenReview.net.

Terry Yue Zhuo, Zhuang Li, Yujin Huang, Yuan-Fang Li, Weiqing Wang, Gholamreza Haffari, and Fatemeh Shiri. 2023. On robustness of prompt-based semantic parsing with large pre-trained language model: An empirical study on codex. *CoRR*, abs/2301.12868.

Proceedings of the 22nd China National Conference on Computational Linguistics, pages 9-16, Harbin, China, August 3 - 5, 2023.

Studying Language Processing in the Human Brain with Speech and Language Models

Chao Zhang
Tsinghua University
University College London
cz277@tsinghua.edu.cn

Andrew Thwaites
University College London
University of Cambridge
acgt2@cam.ac.uk

Cai Wingfield
University of Cambridge
cw417@cam.ac.uk

Abstract

Speech and language computational models have been instrumental in advancing Artificial Intelligence in recent years. However, it remains an open question whether the human brain is employing similar approaches to these models. This tutorial aims to provide an accessible introduction to the extensive research on this topic, specifically focusing on studies that seek to establish quantitative correlations between neuroimaging data from human subjects and the output of language models or automatic speech recognition systems. The tutorial covers various aspects of this research, including a brief overview of brain-computer interfaces and neuroscience, common techniques for data processing and pattern analysis, and representative research examples. Finally, the tutorial addresses the main limitations and technical challenges encountered in this field, as well as the relationship between brain mechanism research and brain-inspired artificial intelligence.

1 Motivation and Objectives

The ability to engage in complex verbal communication is a defining capacity that distinguishes humans from other animals, and speech is a primary medium through which this is achieved. The brain recognises individual words and understands the semantics of sentences through the progressive processing of speech signals, a process known as language comprehension. Understanding the mechanisms underlying this process is an important research topic in computational cognitive neuroscience (Chomsky, 1965; Goldberg, 2006). Computational cognitive neuroscience is a field that connects the brain's complex biological neural system with computational models that can describe and simulate its cognitive functions. Technological developments over the last three decades have aided this field. First, modern neuroimaging technology allows us to collect brain activity patterns ("brain responses"), from human subjects while they receive natural language input. Second, human-level automatic speech recognition (ASR) systems and their accompanying language models can provide human-level model responses to any arbitrary inputs of speech or text. By employing spatiotemporal pattern analysis techniques, we can quantitatively correlate the brain responses and model responses given the same input, providing insights into the brain's spoken language recognition and comprehension mechanisms (Wingfield et al., 2017; Wingfield et al., 2022; Tuckute et al., 2022; Vaidya et al., 2022; Vaidya et al., 2022; Caucheteux et al., 2023). This research method not only provides new means to uncover the secrets of the brain's language comprehension mechanism but also provides a basis for measuring the brain-likeness of models (Wingfield et al., 2022), which can be used both for investigating the intelligence characteristics of the brain and in interpretable artificial intelligence (AI) research. Moreover, the development of connectionism/deep learning AI technology, including large language models (LLMs), continues to draw inspiration from neuroscience, reflecting the close correlation between the two.

This tutorial will mainly introduce the following:

- Brain-computer interface and basics of neuroscience.
- Common data processing and pattern analysis techniques.

Proceedings of the 22nd China National Conference on Computational Linguistics, pages 17-23, Harbin, China, August 3 - 5, 2023.

- Language models and automatic speech recognition technologies.
- Representative research work and its research achievements.
- Major technical challenges and prospects for future work.

2 Tutorial Overview and Structure

2.1 Brain-computer interface and basics of neuroscience (15 min)

While several technologies allow the direct or indirect measurement of human brain responses through non-invasive means, electroencephalography (EEG), magnetoencephalography (MEG), and functional magnetic resonance imaging (fMRI) are three of the most common. EEG and MEG directly measure the accompanying electric field and magnetic field of neuronal dendrites during the generation of action potentials, while fMRI indirectly measures the energy consumption of neurons performing computations by measuring blood oxygen levels. Functional near-infrared spectroscopy (fNIRS) also measures blood oxygen levels, but via local spectroscopy rather than magnetic resonance imaging, which restricts its utility.

Intracranial EEG (iEEG) is less common, due to its requirement for invasive surgery. iEEG technologies include stent EEG (where EEG electrodes are placed inside arteries or veins adjacent to the cortex) and electrocorticography (ECoG), where electrodes are placed directly into the cortex. Intracranial electrode types can range from single-pin electrodes to complex arrays comprised of thousands of miniaturised microelectrodes (Steinmetz et al., 2021).

2.2 Common data processing and pattern analysis techniques (15 min)

Before conducting model-brain comparisons, it is often necessary to clean brain activity data, especially for electrophysiological measurements from EEG and MEG. This involves steps such as averaging, filtering, and removing signal components deemed to arise from non-neuronal activity. For EEG and MEG, the data may also need to be transformed from "sensor space" (where each measurement represents sensor readings over time) to an estimation of "source space" activity (where each measurement corresponds to neural activity in a specific brain location). This transformation is known as "source localisation"(Hämäläinen and Ilmoniemi, 1994).

Comparing neural activity with computational models can be achieved in various ways. The goal is to assess the similarity between a model's behaviour and brain activity, either explicitly or implicitly. The most straightforward techniques simply compare the model's outputs directly with the activity in each brain location. This comparison can be done using similarity metrics like Pearson's Rho, Euclidean distance, or mutual information (*e.g.* (Thwaites et al., 2017; Pérez et al., 2022)).

Such direct comparison requires the model to make specific predictions about each region's activity. If the model is unable to make such a prediction, then the researcher might choose to train a wrapper model that transforms the output of the original model to match the neural data (*e.g.*, (Caucheteux et al., 2023; Oota et al., 2023)). Alternatively, they might choose to relax the constraint that the model's output must match a single location, either by fitting a wrapper model that tries to learn the relationship between multiple locations of activity and the model (using classification or linear regression (Millan et al., 2002)) or by indirectly comparing the patterns of how both the models and brain regions reacted under certain conditions, an approach known as representation similarity analysis (RSA) (Kriegeskorte et al., 2008).[1]

Relaxing the constraint of direct comparison between model and activity has numerous drawbacks, however, including a decrease in statistical power and interpretability.

2.3 Language models and automatic speech recognition technologies (20 min)

Two broad families of computational models are usually considered relevant to the study of the brain's speech recognition and understanding mechanisms: text-based language models and speech-based ASR

[1]The family of approaches that relaxes the "single region constraint" is known as "multivariate pattern analysis" (MVPA) (Haxby, 2012).

Proceedings of the 22nd China National Conference on Computational Linguistics, pages 17-23, Harbin, China, August 3 - 5, 2023.

models. Text-based language models have been found to be useful models for both human language syntax and semantics. GloVe (Pennington et al., 2014) and word2vec (Mikolov et al., 1997) are commonly used word vectors. Pre-trained language models based on the Transformer structure (Vaswani et al., 2017) have profoundly influenced the development of AI, which include embeddings from language models (ELMo) (Peters et al., 2018), Generative pretrained Transformer (GPT) (Radford et al., 2018), bidirectional encoder representations from Transformers (BERT) (Devlin et al., 2019), GPT-2 (Radford et al., 2019), and GPT-3 (Brown et al., 2020), *etc.* In particular, LLMs represented by ChatGPT (OpenAI, 2022) demonstrate powerful multi-task capabilities in language and are considered a milestone in general AI.

ASR is the AI task that most resemble the speech recognition ability of the brain. The development of ASR technology has gone through two stages: systems based on hidden Markov models (HMM) and end-to-end systems. Modular systems include acoustic models, language models, pronunciation dictionaries, and decoding programs (Jelinek, 1998), commonly using Gaussian mixture models (GMM) and ANN to model the observation probability of HMM (Young et al., 2015; Bourlard and Morgan, 1994; Hinton et al., 2012). ASR models that only use ANN models without HMM appeared as early as the late 1980s (Robinson and Fallside, 1987), but it has only recently gradually and completely replaced HMM models as the mainstream method. Connectionist temporal classification (CTC) is a popular pure neural network ASR method (Graves et al., 2006) equivalent to an ANN-HMM (Li et al., 2019). End-to-end ASR uses an ANN model to directly convert the input speech sequence to the output text sequence (Graves, 2012; Graves et al., 2013; Chorowski et al., 2015; Lu et al., 2015; Chan et al., 2016). The end-to-end ASR have added a memory mechanism for elements in the output word sequence to model at the sentence and semantic levels like text language models, equivalent to audio-grounded language models (Li et al., 2019), and can fully utilize audio information for speech understanding (Sun et al., 2023). However, even large end-to-end ASR models trained with a massive amount of speech data still have a significant gap in accuracy and robustness in real applications compared to humans (Zhang et al., 2022; Radford et al., 2022). Consequently, studying the brain's speech recognition and understanding mechanisms is of great value in inspiring improvements in ASR (Wingfield et al., 2022).

2.4 Representative research work and its research achievements (30 min)

Humans consume language via different means, and the study of the brain's language comprehension mechanism is consequently also wide-ranging. For example, reading text is a common experimental method in neuroscience research for language cognition. By using fMRI to collect blood oxygen level signals when subjects read words and pictures, Mitchell et al. in 2008 demonstrated that word vectors constructed based on co-occurrence frequency are able to predict brain responses related to isolated words (Mitchell et al., 2008). Wehbe and colleagues built on this idea and used more natural narrative text as stimuli to study lexical features (Wehbe et al., 2014) and syntactic features (Reddy and Wehbe, 2021). Wehbe et al. also used MEG data with high temporal precision and established a correspondence between the MEG data and word vectors of the RNN language model by learning a linear mapping function (Wehbe et al., 2014). More recent studies have increasingly used neuroimaging data such as EEG and MEG with high temporal precision (Toneva et al., 2020; Hollenstein N et al., 2021; Schrimpf et al., 2021; Chehab et al., Data Analysis; Toneva et al., 2022; Caucheteux and King, 2022; Murphy et al., 2022), as well as vector representations derived from text models like word2vec, GloVe, ELMo, GPT, BERT, and GPT-2. These studies show that language models can be used to interpret the brain's language-processing mechanisms, thereby enhancing our understanding of human language cognition.

Having subjects listen to narrative speech is more natural than reading text, as speech inherently has temporality, making it easier to determine the order and duration of responses to individual words. In 2014, Mesgarani et al. had epilepsy patients listen to natural continuous speech and used intracranial electrodes to record brain electrical signals with high spatiotemporal precision, finding that the superior temporal cortex of the brain concentrated speech features (Mesgarani et al., 2014). Later, Wingfield and others found commonalities between humans and ASR based on GMM-HMM acoustic models in simultaneously collected EEG and MEG data, including significant correlations between both phonetic

Proceedings of the 22nd China National Conference on Computational Linguistics, pages 17-23, Harbin, China, August 3 - 5, 2023.

features and the hidden layers of the DNN-HMM acoustic model with those areas of the brain related to auditory and phonetic processing (Wingfield et al., 2016; Wingfield et al., 2017; Wingfield et al., 2022). Défossez and others found that using comparative learning of brain responses collected by EEG or MEG when listening to speech and the pre-trained wav2vec 2.0 model's responses could achieve top-1 and top-10 classification accuracy rates of up to 44.1% and 72.5% respectively from 1,594 3-second speech segments heard by the subject (Défossez et al., 2022). The increased interest in audio-based ASR as a computational model has partially dampened the interest in fMRI recordings (which have a relatively poor temporal resolution compared with EEG and MEG), and ASR-related studies in EEG and MEG are gradually increasing (Wang et al., 2022).

In China, many universities and research institutions have made significant research achievements in the neural mechanisms of language cognition (Wang et al., 2022; Lu et al., 2019; Zou et al., 2022; Wang et al., 2020; Zhang et al., 2022; Fu et al., 2022; Qian et al., 2016; Liu et al., 2022; Jin et al., 2018; Sheng et al., 2019). Although the development of ASR and LLMs in China is broadly synchronized with the world's leading edge, there is relatively less research on using these AI computational models to parse brain language cognition mechanisms, most of which use reading text rather than listening to speech as stimuli (Zou et al., 2022; Wang et al., 2020). The team of researchers Shaonan Wang and Chengqing Zong from the Institute of Automation of the Chinese Academy of Sciences used open-source fMRI data based on listening to English narrative speech, and used ELMo and BERT language models to study the representation of different syntactic features in the brain (Zhang et al., 2022), and in 2022, they released Chinese data collected with fMRI and MEG respectively (Wang et al., 2022).

2.5 Major technical challenges and prospects for future work (10 min)

Research on human brain language cognition mechanisms using ASR and language models is a complex interdisciplinary field of neuroscience and AI, involving various fundamental sciences such as physics, statistics, physiology, neuroscience, psychology, and linguistics, as well as advanced hardware and software technologies such as brain-computer interfaces, signal processing, machine learning, and multivoxel pattern analysis. The diversity of the disciplines involved is high, and many technologies (such as AI and brain-computer interfaces) are not yet fully mature, resulting in the facing of many technical challenges. However, such disciplinary characteristics also bring important scientific opportunities and many new application opportunities. In the medical field, relevant research methods and results can help understand and treat brain diseases related to speech (such as autism and dementia); in the field of human-computer interaction, it can be significant to the development of brain-computer interfaces based on imagined speech.

3 The Presenter and Co-Authors

Chao Zhang (presenter, presentation in Mandarin) is a tenure-track Assistant Professor at the Department of Electronic Engineering at Tsinghua University and holds an Honorary Professorship at University College London. He obtained both his BEng and MSc degrees from Tsinghua University and his PhD degree from Cambridge University. He was a research scientist at Google.

Andrew Thwaites (co-author) is a Senior Research Fellow at UCL and Affiliated Lecturer in Statistics at the University of Cambridge's Department of Psychology. His research focuses on computational neuroscience, in particular speech and auditory processing. Dr Thwaites received his PhD in Computational Neuroscience from the University of Cambridge.

Cai Wingfield (co-author) is a Visiting Scientist at the University of Cambridge (MRC Cognition and Brain Sciences Unit). His research focuses on speech and language processing, as well as on the dual roles of language and simulation in conceptual cognition. He received his PhD in the mathematical foundations of computer science at the University of Bath.

Proceedings of the 22nd China National Conference on Computational Linguistics, pages 17-23, Harbin, China, August 3 - 5, 2023.

References

N. Chomsky. 1965. *Aspects of the Theory of Syntax*. MIT Press.

A. Goldberg. 2006. *Constructions at Work: The Nature of Generalization in Language*. Oxford University Press.

C. Wingfield, L. Su, B. Devereux, X. Liu, C. Zhang, P. Woodland, E. Fonteneau, A. Thwaites, W. Marslen-Wilson. 2016. Multi-level representations in speech processing in brain and machine: Evidence from EMEG and RSA. in *Society for the Neurobiology of Language*.

C. Wingfield, L. Su, X. Liu, et al. 2017. Relating dynamic brain states to dynamic machine states: Human and machine solutions to the speech recognition problem. *PloS Computational Biology*, 13:e1005617.

C. Wingfield, C. Zhang, B. Devereux, et al. 2022. On the similarities of representations in artificial and brain neural networks for speech recognition. *Frontiers in Computational Neuroscience*:16.

G. Tuckute, J. Feather, D. Boebinger, et al. 2022. Many but not all deep neural network audio models capture brain responses and exhibit hierarchical region correspondence. *bioRxiv:2022.09.06.506680*.

A.R. Vaidya, S. Jain, A. Huth. 2022. Self-supervised models of audio effectively explain human cortical responses to speech. in *Proc. ICML*.

C. Caucheteux, A. Gramfort, J.R. King. 2023. Evidence of a predictive coding hierarchy in the human brain listening to speech. *Natural Human Behaviour*:10.1038/s41562-022-01516-2.

N. A. Steinmetz, C. Aydin, A. Lebedeva, M. Okun et al. 2021. Neuropixels 2.0: A miniaturized high-density probe for stable, long-term brain recordings. *Science*, 372:abf4588.

J. Pennington, R. Socher, C.D. Manning. 2014. GloVe: Global vectors for word representation. in *Proc. EMNLP*.

T. Mikolov, I. Sutskever, K. Chen, et al. 2013. Distributed representations of words and phrases and their compositionality. in *Proc. NIPS*.

S. Hochreiter, J. Schmidhuber. 1997. Long short-term memory. *Neural Computation*, 9:1735-1780.

M.E. Peters, M. Neumann, M. Iyyer, et al. 2018. Deep contextualized word representations. in *Proc. NAACL-HLT*.

R. Bommasani, D.A. Hudson, E. Adeli, et al. 2021. On the opportunities and risks of foundation models. *arXiv preprint arXiv:2108.07258*.

A. Radford, K. Narasimhan, T. Salimans, et al. 2018. Improving language understanding by generative pre-training. *OpenAI blog*.

J. Devlin, M.-W. Chang, K. Lee, K. Toutanova. 2019. BERT: Pre-training of deep bidirectional transformers for language understanding. in *Proc. NAACL-HLT*.

A. Radford, J. Wu, R. Child, et al. 2019. Language models are unsupervised multitask learners. *OpenAI blog*.

T. Brown, B. Mann, N. Ryder, et al. 2020. Language models are few-shot learners. in *Proc. NeurIPS*.

A. Vaswani, N. Shazeer, N. Parmar, et al. 2017. Attention is all you need. in *Proc. NIPS*.

OpenAI. 2022. Introducing ChatGPT. *OpenAI Blog*.

F. Jelinek. 1998. *Statistical Methods for Speech Recognition*. MIT Press.

S. Young, G. Evermann, M. Gales. 2015. *The HTK Book (for HTK version 3.5)*. Cambridge University Engineering Department.

H. Bourlard, N. Morgan. 1994. *Connectionist Speech Recognition: A Hybrid Approach*. Springer Science & Business Media.

G. Hinton, L. Deng, D. Yu, et al. 2012. Deep neural networks for acoustic modeling in speech recognition: The shared views of four research groups. *IEEE Signal Processing Magazine*, 29:82-97.

A.J. Robinson, F. Fallside. 1987. The Utility Driven Dynamic Error Propagation Network. *Cambridge University Engineering Department*.

Proceedings of the 22nd China National Conference on Computational Linguistics, pages 17-23, Harbin, China, August 3 - 5, 2023.

A. Graves, S. Fernández, F. Gomez, et al. 2006. Connectionist temporal classification: Labelling unsegmented sequence data with recurrent neural networks. in *Proc. ICML.*

Q. Li, C. Zhang, P.C. Woodland. 2019. Integrating source-channel and attention-based sequence-to-sequence models for speech recognition. in *Proc. ASRU.*

A. Graves. 2012. Sequence transduction with recurrent neural networks. in *Proc. ICML.*

A. Graves, A. Mohamed, G. Hinton. 2013. Speech recognition with deep recurrent neural networks. in *Proc. ICASSP.*

J.K. Chorowski, D. Bahdanau, D. Serdyuk, et al. 2015. Attention-based models for speech recognition. in *Proc. NIPS.*

L. Lu, X. Zhang, K. Cho, et al. 2015. A study of the recurrent neural network encoder-decoder for large vocabulary speech recognition. in *Proc. Interspeech.*

W. Chan, N. Jaitly, Q. Le, et al. 2016. Listen, attend and spell: A neural network for large vocabulary conversational speech recognition. in *Proc. ICASSP.*

G. Sun, C. Zhang, I. Vulić, P. Budzianowski, P.C. Woodland 2023. Knowledge-Aware Audio-Grounded Generative Slot Filling for Limited Annotated Data. *arXiv preprint arXiv:2307.01764.*

Y. Zhang, D.S. Park, W. Han, et al. 2022. BigSSL: Exploring the frontier of large-scale semi-supervised learning for automatic speech recognition. *IEEE Journal of Selected Topics in Signal Processing*, 16:1519-1532.

A. Radford, J.W. Kim, T. Xu, et al. 2022. Robust speech recognition via large-scale weak supervision. *arXiv preprint arXiv:2212.04356.*

T.M. Mitchell, S.V. Shinkareva, A. Carlson, et al. 2008. Predicting human brain activity associated with the meanings of nouns. *Science*, 320:1191-1195.

L. Wehbe, B. Murphy, P. Talukdar, et al. 2014. Simultaneously uncovering the patterns of brain regions involved in different story reading subprocesses. *PloS one*, 9:e112575.

A.J. Reddy, L. Wehbe. 2021. Can fMRI reveal the representation of syntactic structure in the brain?. in *Proc. NeurIPS.*

L. Wehbe, A. Vaswani, K. Knight, et al. 2014. Aligning context-based statistical models of language with brain activity during reading. in *Proc. EMNLP.*

M. Toneva, O. Stretcu, B. Póczos, et al. 2020. Modeling task effects on meaning representation in the brain via zero-shot meg prediction. in *Proc. NeurIPS.*

N. Hollenstein N, C. Renggli, B. Glaus, et al. 2021. Decoding EEG brain activity for multi-modal natural language processing. *Frontiers in Human Neuroscience*:378.

M. Schrimpf, I.A. Blank, G. Tuckute, et al. 2021. The neural architecture of language: Integrative modeling converges on predictive processing. *Proceedings of the National Academy of Sciences*, 118:e2105646118.

O. Chehab, A. Défossez, L. Jean-Christophe, et al. 2022. Deep recurrent encoder: An end-to-end network to model magnetoencephalography at scale. *Neurons, Behavior, Data Analysis, and Theory*

M. Toneva, T.M. Mitchell, L. Wehbe. 2022. Combining computational controls with natural text reveals aspects of meaning composition. *Nature Computatonal Science*, 2:745-757.

C. Caucheteux, J.R. King. 2022. Brains and algorithms partially converge in natural language processing. *Communications Biology*, 5:134.

A. Murphy, B. Bohnet, R. McDonald, U. Noppeney. 2022. Decoding part-of-speech from human EEG signals. in *Proc. ACL.*

N. Mesgarani, C. Cheung, K. Johnson, et al. 2014. Phonetic feature encoding in human superior temporal gyrus. *Science*, 343:1006-1010.

A. Défossez, C. Caucheteux, J. Rapin, et al. 2022. Decoding speech from non-invasive brain recordings. *arXiv preprint arXiv:2208.12266.*

Proceedings of the 22nd China National Conference on Computational Linguistics, pages 17-23, Harbin, China, August 3 - 5, 2023.

S. Wang, X. Zhang, J. Zhang, et al. 2022. A synchronized multimodal neuroimaging dataset for studying brain language processing. *Scientific Data*, 9:590.

L. Lu, Q. Wang, J. Sheng, et al. 2019. Neural tracking of speech mental imagery during rhythmic inner counting. *Elife*, 8:e48971.

S. Zou, S. Wang, J. Zhang, et al. 2022. Cross-modal cloze task: A new task to brain-to-word decoding. *Findings of the ACL.*

S. Wang, J. Zhang, N. Lin, et al. 2020. Probing brain activation patterns by dissociating semantics and syntax in sentences. in *Proc. AAAI.*

X. Zhang, S. Wang, N. Lin, et al. 2022. Probing word syntactic representations in the brain by a feature elimination method. in *Proc. AAAI.*

Z. Fu, X. Wang, X. Wang, et al. 2022. Different computational relations in language are captured by distinct brain systems. *Cerebral Cortex.*

P. Qian, X. Qiu, X. Huang. 2016. Bridging LSTM architecture and the neural dynamics during reading. in *Proc. IJCAI.*

Y. Liu, C. Luo, J. Zheng, et al. 2022. Working memory asymmetrically modulates auditory and linguistic processing of speech. *NeuroImage*, 264:119698.

P. Jin, J. Zou, T. Zhou, et al. 2018. Eye activity tracks task-relevant structures during speech and auditory sequence perception. *Nature Communications*, 9:5374.

J. Sheng, L. Zheng, B. Lyu, et al. 2019. The cortical maps of hierarchical linguistic structures during speech perception. *Cerebral Cortex*, 29:3232-3240.

M.S. Hämäläinen, R.J. Ilmoniemi. 1994. Interpreting magnetic fields of the brain: Minimum norm estimates. *Medical & Biological Engineering & Computing*, 32:35–42.

J. Millan, J. Mouriño, M. Franzé, F. Cincotti, M. Varsta, J. Heikkonen, and F. Babiloni. 2002. A local neural classifier for the recognition of EEG patterns associated to mental tasks. *IEEE Transactions on Neural Networks*, 13:678-686.

N. Kriegeskorte, M. Mur, and P.A. Bandettini. 2008. Representational similarity analysis-connecting the branches of systems neuroscience. *Frontiers in Systems Neuroscience*:4.

A. Thwaites, J. Schlittenlacher, I. Nimmo-Smith, W.D. Marslen-Wilson, B.C.J. Moore. 2017. Tonotopic representation of loudness in the human cortex. *Hearing Research*, 344:244–254.

A. Pérez, M.H. Davis, R.A.A. Ince, H. Zhang, Z. Fu, M. Lamarca, M.A. Lambon Ralph, P.J. Monahan. 2022. Timing of brain entrainment to the speech envelope during speaking, listening and self-listening. *Cognition*, 224.

S. R. Oota, K. Pahwa, M. Marreddy, M. Gupta, B. S. Raju. 2023. Neural Architecture of Speech. in *Proc. ICASSP*.

J. V. Haxby. 2012. Multivariate pattern analysis of fMRI: The early beginnings. in *Neuroimage*, 62:852-52012.

Proceedings of the 22nd China National Conference on Computational Linguistics, pages 17-23, Harbin, China, August 3 - 5, 2023.

Foundation Models for Robotics: Best Known Practices

Shaocong Xu, Hao Zhao
Tsinghua University, AIR
xushaocong@stu.xmu.edu.cn, zhaohao@air.tsinghua.edu.cn

Abstract

Artificial general intelligence (AGI) used to be a sci-fi word but recently the surprising generalization capability of foundation models have triggered a lot of attention to AGI, in both academia and industry. Large language models can now answer questions or chat with human beings, using fluent sentences and clear reasoning. Diffusion models can now draw pictures of unprecedented photo-realism, according to human commands and controls. Researchers have also made substantial efforts to explore new possibilities for robotics applications with the help of foundation models. Since this interdisciplinary field is still under fast development, there is no clear methodological conclusions for now. In this tutorial, I will briefly go through **best known practices** that have shown transformative capabilities in several sub-fields. Specifically, there are five representative paradigms: (1) Using foundation models to allow human-friendly human-car interaction; (2) Using foundation models to equip robots the capabilities of understanding vague human needs; (3) Using foundation models to break down complex tasks into achievable sub-tasks; (4) Using foundation models to composite skill primitives so that reinforcement learning can work with sparse rewards; (5) Using foundation models to bridge languge commands and low-level control dynamics. I hope these best known practices to inspire NLP researchers.

1 Introduction

This is a tutorial paper that summarizes my talk at CCL 2023, on the topic of *Foundation models for robotics: best known practices*. The concept of foundation models emerge in the community of natural language processing (NLP), like GPT (Brown et al., 2020). Current foundation models can learn language skills using few shots and notably without fine-tuning the model (known as in-context learning). This human-like behavior has not been demonstrated before and widely considered as an encouraging step towards artificial general intelligence (AGI). However, a long-existing problem still lingers around at the age of foundation models, which is known as the Moravec's paradox. Specifically speaking, high-level human intelligence like language and reasoning actually consumes relatively less computation while low-level control is much more complicated than one may think. This paradox is echoed by the current state of AI research: while language models are getting stronger and stronger, robots still struggle to move and manipulate, at least in the context of artificial general intelligence.

Despite the disappointing situation as described by the Moravec's paradox, we see a line of encouraging research efforts related to foundation models that have definitely expanded the scope of robotics research. As a disclaimer, this does not mean that the paradox is solved. Specifically, we observe several promising paradigms that successfully marry robotics with the recent progress of foundation models, among which five representative works are covered in this tutorial: (1) Using foundation models to allow human-friendly human-car interaction; (2) Using foundation models to equip robots the capabilities of understanding vague human needs; (3) Using foundation models to break down complex tasks into achievable sub-tasks; (4) Using foundation models to composite skill primitives so that reinforcement learning can work with sparse rewards; (5) Using foundation models to bridge languge commands and low-level control dynamics. Apart from these five topics, other smaller ones w.r.t. open-set understand-

Proceedings of the 22nd China National Conference on Computational Linguistics, pages 24-29, Harbin, China, August 3 - 5, 2023.

ing (Liu et al., 2023) or anomaly detection (Tian et al., 2023) do exist although they are not covered.

2 Best Known Practices

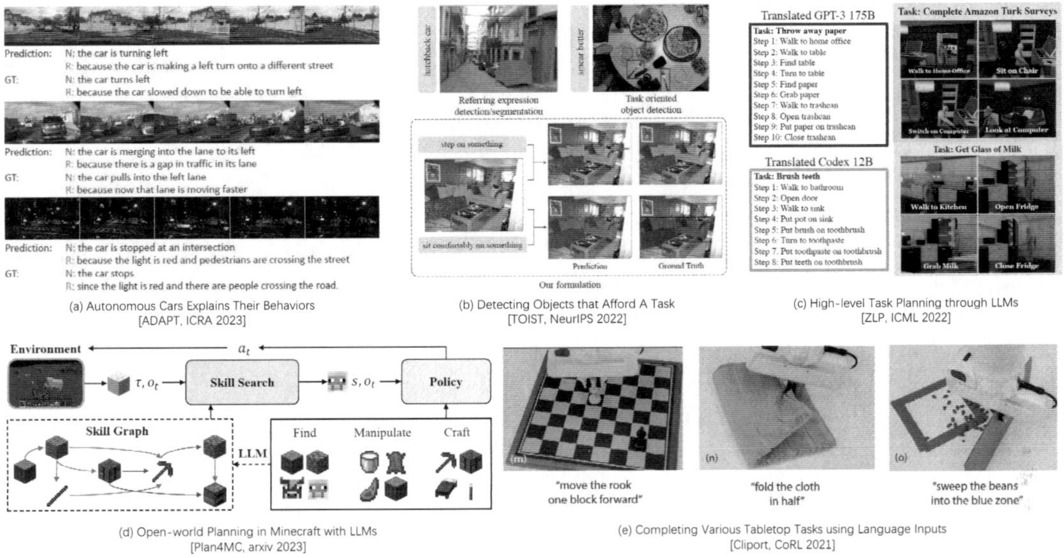

(a) Autonomous Cars Explains Their Behaviors [ADAPT, ICRA 2023]
(b) Detecting Objects that Afford A Task [TOIST, NeurIPS 2022]
(c) High-level Task Planning through LLMs [ZLP, ICML 2022]
(d) Open-world Planning in Minecraft with LLMs [Plan4MC, arxiv 2023]
(e) Completing Various Tabletop Tasks using Language Inputs [Cliport, CoRL 2021]

Figure 1: Foundation models including large language models (LLMs) and large vision-language models (VLMs) have enabled new capabilities in various robotics tasks, as demonstrated in this figure. These new progresses come in different paradigms and these five methods represent the **best known practices**. Specifically speaking, (a) ADAPT (Jin et al., 2023) allows autonomous driving cars to describe and explain their own behaviors using natural language. (b) TOIST (Li et al., 2022a) equips robots with the ability to find an object that affords any tasks specified by natural language. (c) ZLP (Huang et al., 2022) exploits large language models to break down high-level commands into step-by-step action primitives. (d) Plan4MC (Yuan et al., 2023) combines skill primitives using large language models so that agents can learn to accomplish diverse tasks in Minecraft with sparse rewards. (e) Cliport (Shridhar et al., 2022) separates the pathways for language and affordance so that the agents can accomplish manipulation tasks according to any natural language commands and transfer their skills to real worlds seamlessly.

As shown in Fig. 1, we demonstrate five paradigms that foundation models can benefit robotic perception, planning and control. It is far from an extensive list but reasonably representative.

2.1 Talking with agents

Talking with agent is an potential practices of using vision-language foundation models (VLMs). There are several representative works in this direction. Firstly, ADAPT (Jin et al., 2023) is an algorithm that allows autonomous cars to simultaneously describe their behaviors and explain the rationale behind. While robotaxis are now running smoothly in large cities, the experience is still far from that of taking a taxi driven by human beings. A notable difference is that human drivers can tell the passengers why they drive in a certain manner thus comforting the passenger. ADAPT can tell the passenger that the car is stopping because of red traffic lights and pedestrians ahead (Fig. 1-a last row), which enhances human trust on robotic systems.

Additionally, SPRING (Long et al., 2023) is an algorithm that enables agents to describe their responses not only based on the attributes of objects (the black jacket) in the scene, but also on the spatial

Proceedings of the 22nd China National Conference on Computational Linguistics, pages 24-29, Harbin, China, August 3 - 5, 2023.
(c) Technical Committee on Computational Linguistics, Chinese Information Processing Society of China

relations of the objects (the black jacket on the leftmost floor rack). Such method is particularly useful when the agent is faced with an extremely complex situation.

Furthermore, SQA3D (Ma et al., 2022) decomposes the question answering task into situation localization and answering. The response to the question 'What is the object situated behind the apple that is currently positioned in front of you?' is dependent on the agent's situation. Failure to account for this factor results in agent performance falling short of human expectations in real-world embodied environments. SQA3D allows the agent to learn how to adapt to various situations and execute different commands issued by humans.

Thus, the applications of VLMs for human-robot interaction have the potential to alleviate Moravec's Paradox. We hope that further research efforts can be dedicated to this area.

2.2 Finding tools for any tasks

TOIST (Li et al., 2022a) is an algorithm that finds tools and segments their masks in visual inputs, according to any task specification, shown in Fig. 1-b. The task specification is given by natural language like a verb phrase *sit comfortably on*, so that it breaks the bottleneck of prior closed-set affordance understanding models. It leverages vision-language foundation models that understand well nouns but further distill the representation into pronouns and allow the understanding of verbs in an open-set manner. Using this model, intelligent robots can find tools that serve a human commander's vague goals without the need of exactly providing the tool's name.

The Touch-line transformer algorithm (Li et al., 2022b) is another representative work that can localize the objects both referred by natural language and indicated by the virtual touch line of human. Thus, This method endows VLMs with the capability to comprehend human gestures and accurately locate objects indicated by those gestures.

2.3 Breaking down high-level commands.

Just like the problem that TOIST addresses, a long-term goal of robotics is to fulfill high-level commands from human beings. While TOIST finds tools to serve a certain task, zero-shot language planner (ZLP (Huang et al., 2022) as shown in Fig. 1-c) can leverage the reasonging power of language foundation models to break down high-level commands into practical sub-tasks. For example, to achieve the task of brushing teeth, eight steps are needed and foundation models can be easily instructed to do this decomposition job in a zero-shot manner (shown in Fig. 1-d). Finally, a robot can conduct sub-tasks with pre-built motion primitives.

Similar to ZLP, SPLL (Sharma et al., 2021) utilizes the reasoning capabilities of language foundation models to decompose high-level language abstractions into several primitive low-level actions. This approach creatively leverages pre-trained language models to facilitate the acquisition of new skills by enabling the agent to reason about the underlying task structure and generate effective action plans.

2.4 Escaping the curse of sparse rewards

Reinforcement learning is widely considered as another promising path towards artificial general intelligence. If an agent can experience the world thousands of times in a realistic simulator, it can finally learn generic low-level control and high-level reasoning skills. However, apart from the realism problem, reinforcement learning usually suffers from the issue of sparse rewards when conducting complicated tasks. Plan4MC (Yuan et al., 2023) creatively combines low-level skill learning and the skill graphs pre-generated by language foundation models to effectively accomplish tasks under the guidance of very sparse rewards. ELLA (Mirchandani et al., 2021) leverages learned language abstractions to provide more accurate reward signals and enhance the agent's ability to learn and accomplish tasks effectively.

2.5 Versatile and clever hands that listen to your commands

While research works mentioned above focus on perception or relatively high-level planning, Cliport (Shridhar et al., 2022) is a method that successfully allows robot arms to accomplish diverse low-level control tasks according any human commands specified by natural language, as shown in Fig. 1-e. The architecture disentagles semantics and spatial information while conditioning two streams on language

Proceedings of the 22nd China National Conference on Computational Linguistics, pages 24-29, Harbin, China, August 3 - 5, 2023.

representations generated by foundation models. Since the motion primitive is simplified as a bin-picking formulation, 2D affordance maps allow the network to achieve open-set tasks. Interestingly, this system exhibits good sim-to-real generalization capabilities and functions as a versatile and clever hand that listens to your arbitrary commands. PA (Shridhar et al., 2023) is another representative work that can effectively train a model to perform a total of 25 robotic manipulation tasks, including 18 RLBench tasks with 249 variations and 7 real-world tasks with 18 variations, using only a few natural language descriptions per task. This approach creatively leverages language-conditioned behavioral cloning to enable the agent to reason about task structures and generate effective action plans.

3 Tutorial Outline

Part I: Introduction (20 min)

- The development of large language models
- The definition of the Moravec's paradox
- Promising paradigms ellivate the Moravec's paradox
  - Talking with agents
  - Finding tools for any tasks
  - Breaking down high-level commands
  - Escaping the curse of sparse rewards
  - Versatile and clever hands that listen to your commands

Part II: Best Known Practices (60 min)

- Talking with agent
- Finding tools for any tasks
- Breaking down high-level commands
- Escaping the curse of sparse rewards
- Versatile and clever hands that listen to your commands

Part III: Conclusion (10 min)

4 Reading List

1. ADAPT: Action-aware Driving Caption Transformer (Jin et al., 2023);
2. TOIST: Task Oriented Instance Segmentation Transformer with Noun-Pronoun Distillation (Li et al., 2022a);
3. Language Models as Zero-Shot Planners: Extracting Actionable Knowledge for Embodied Agents (Huang et al., 2022);
4. Plan4MC: Skill Reinforcement Learning and Planning for Open-World Minecraft Tasks (Yuan et al., 2023);
5. CLIPort: What and Where Pathways for Robotic Manipulation (Shridhar et al., 2022);

Proceedings of the 22nd China National Conference on Computational Linguistics, pages 24-29, Harbin, China, August 3 - 5, 2023.

5 Instructor

Hao Zhao is an assistant professor at Tsinghua University, where he leads a research group focused on computer vision fields related to robotics, particularly 3D scene understanding. Prior to joining Tsinghua University, he was a research scientist at Intel Labs China and a joint postdoc affiliated with Peking University. He obtained his Ph.D. and Bachelor's degrees from the Department of Electronic Engineering at Tsinghua University. Additionally, he is proud to have served as a former leader of Skyworks, the largest robotics club at THU, where he contributed significantly to the growth of the club and fostered a culture of innovation and excellence.

In addition to his academic work, Hao Zhao has also been involved in entrepreneurship, co-launching more than 10 startups in various fields such as social networks, web development tools, unmanned aerial vehicles, intelligent delivery, smart grid, VR devices, virtual human, cloud design, autonomous driving, and smart manufacturing since 2009.

His homepage can be found at `https://sites.google.com/view/fromandto`

Acknowledgements

This tutorial substantially benefits from the suggestions of Prof. Hao Dong in Peking University.

References

Tom Brown, Benjamin Mann, Nick Ryder, Melanie Subbiah, Jared D Kaplan, Prafulla Dhariwal, Arvind Neelakantan, Pranav Shyam, Girish Sastry, Amanda Askell, et al. 2020. Language models are few-shot learners. *Advances in neural information processing systems*, 33:1877–1901.

Wenlong Huang, Pieter Abbeel, Deepak Pathak, and Igor Mordatch. 2022. Language models as zero-shot planners: Extracting actionable knowledge for embodied agents. In *International Conference on Machine Learning*, pages 9118–9147. PMLR.

Bu Jin, Xinyu Liu, Yupeng Zheng, Pengfei Li, Hao Zhao, Tong Zhang, Yuhang Zheng, Guyue Zhou, and Jingjing Liu. 2023. Adapt: Action-aware driving caption transformer. *arXiv preprint arXiv:2302.00673*.

Pengfei Li, Beiwen Tian, Yongliang Shi, Xiaoxue Chen, Hao Zhao, Guyue Zhou, and Ya-Qin Zhang. 2022a. Toist: Task oriented instance segmentation transformer with noun-pronoun distillation. *Advances in Neural Information Processing Systems*, 35:17597–17611.

Yang Li, Xiaoxue Chen, Hao Zhao, Jiangtao Gong, Guyue Zhou, Federico Rossano, and Yixin Zhu. 2022b. Understanding Embodied Reference with Touch-Line Transformer, October.

Xinyu Liu, Beiwen Tian, Zhen Wang, Rui Wang, Kehua Sheng, Bo Zhang, Hao Zhao, and Guyue Zhou. 2023. Delving into shape-aware zero-shot semantic segmentation. In *Proceedings of the IEEE/CVF Conference on Computer Vision and Pattern Recognition*, pages 2999–3009.

Yuxing Long, Binyuan Hui, Fulong Ye, Yanyang Li, Zhuoxin Han, Caixia Yuan, Yongbin Li, and Xiaojie Wang. 2023. Spring: Situated conversation agent pretrained with multimodal questions from incremental layout graph. *arXiv preprint arXiv:2301.01949*.

Xiaojian Ma, Silong Yong, Zilong Zheng, Qing Li, Yitao Liang, Song-Chun Zhu, and Siyuan Huang. 2022. Sqa3d: Situated question answering in 3d scenes. *arXiv preprint arXiv:2210.07474*.

Suvir Mirchandani, Siddharth Karamcheti, and Dorsa Sadigh. 2021. Ella: Exploration through learned language abstraction. In *Neural Information Processing Systems*.

Pratyusha Sharma, Antonio Torralba, and Jacob Andreas. 2021. Skill induction and planning with latent language. In *Annual Meeting of the Association for Computational Linguistics*.

Mohit Shridhar, Lucas Manuelli, and Dieter Fox. 2022. Cliport: What and where pathways for robotic manipulation. In *Conference on Robot Learning*, pages 894–906. PMLR.

Mohit Shridhar, Lucas Manuelli, and Dieter Fox. 2023. Perceiver-actor: A multi-task transformer for robotic manipulation. In *Conference on Robot Learning*, pages 785–799. PMLR.

Proceedings of the 22nd China National Conference on Computational Linguistics, pages 24-29, Harbin, China, August 3 - 5, 2023.

Computational Linguistics

Beiwen Tian, Mingdao Liu, Huan-ang Gao, Pengfei Li, Hao Zhao, and Guyue Zhou. 2023. Unsupervised road anomaly detection with language anchors. In *2023 IEEE International Conference on Robotics and Automation (ICRA)*, pages 7778–7785. IEEE.

Haoqi Yuan, Chi Zhang, Hongcheng Wang, Feiyang Xie, Penglin Cai, Hao Dong, and Zongqing Lu. 2023. Plan4mc: Skill reinforcement learning and planning for open-world minecraft tasks. *arXiv preprint arXiv:2303.16563*.

Proceedings of the 22nd China National Conference on Computational Linguistics, pages 24-29, Harbin, China, August 3 - 5, 2023.

Association for Computational Linguistics
209 N. Eighth Street
Stroudsburg, Pennsylvania 18360

ISBN 978-1-7138-8991-5

CURRAN ASSOCIATES INC.
proceedings.com

Conference on Empirical Methods in Natural Language Processing (EMNLP 2023)

Tutorial Abstracts

Singapore
6 - 10 December 2023